A Flying Start

By the same author:

My Father: The True Story
The Macdonald Sisters

A Flying Start

A. W. BALDWIN

All service ranks the same with God—
With God, whose puppets, best and worst,
Are we: there is no last nor first.

ROBERT BROWNING—*Pippa Passes*

PETER DAVIES : LONDON

Printed in Great Britain by Cox & Wyman Limited,
London, Fakenham and Reading

Contents

Chapter		Page
1	A Glance Back	1
2	Not Yet Diagnosed	15
3	A Marked Man	31
4	All the Best	55
5	Forgotten Men	87
6	Mismustered	113
7	Sparks	141
8	Remismustered	166
9	Not Wanted	187
10	Not Suited	206

1

A Glance Back

Prince: We must all to the wars, and thy place
shall be honourable.

SHAKESPEARE – *King Henry IV, Part I*

Recruited, sorted, numbered, billeted, the soft conscript of half a day's service in the Royal Air Force lies beside the five other unknown sleeping warriors in the darkness, thinking back along his thirty-eight civilian years.

How shall I fare with these room-mates, and what will they make of me? During the disrobing chatter Welsh accents had predominated. I'm glad of that. Long ago, working in South Wales, I found the people to be generally humorous and understanding. With any luck I shall be all right with them. Yet how shall I accustom myself to this intimate life? At the age of ten it had seemed natural. In those school days we always had to say our prayers before getting into bed. No Sergeant has insisted upon it here. Yet how much more desirable it is on this grim night than ever it was at school.

Out, then and kneel! But what if the black-out lights go on and show me postured like the infant Samuel? Should I then address the room in Hamlet's words? 'For every man hath business and desire, such as it is; and for my own poor part, look you, I'll go pray.'

That 'look you', at any rate, ought to raise an echo from hearts sick for Cambrian valleys. Oh well, the troops must

I

get used to my ways for the duration, as I must get used to theirs.

God help this airman, and these unconscious strangers too, and all their wives and children. And, while I'm about it, I may as well resolve to do the same every night, light or dark, alone or not. I shall need it.

Well, then, that's decided. As from the 6th September, 1941. Signed: 'Theodore Arthur Webland, per pro A/C 2 Webland, 4121107. For the means of grace and for the hope of glory.'

Into sheetless bed again, memories, not dreams, take over. What direction do they face on 4121107's first night? Naturally towards his aptitude for military life.

The Weblands have no military history at all, unless one counts great-uncle Carrington who gruffly brought back Afghan swords and daggers from his service on the Frontier; and his great-grandfather, who rose obliquely from midshipman to clergyman in the space of seven years. No. Going back two hundred years, hardly anything but parsons and manufacturers had fruited on the family tree; and, before that, dull squiredom had been cropped for as far back as need not matter.

It was Roland, the eldest of the family, who as a small boy had found and loved and later lost the war-path, and by the force of his personality had dragged in the others, until by about 1911 the K.R.A. was well established. K.R. is easy: King's Royal. The A stood for Amberdine, which was our home: The King's Royal Amberdines. Whatever Roland introduced was always fairly authentic. Some years later, when he became Thespian and made the same juniors strut the stage with him, it was all done in the proper way, with a professional touch. So it was with soldiering. How he learned it so well is a mystery. There was drill at his school and books to be read; but passion alone made it live; and that he had in plenty. Didn't we all suffer from it?

Most likely his military urge arose because armies and the command of them meant power, and it was necessary for Roland either to lead or to rebel. If he followed the drum it was his own trumpet that he had to blow. I for my part loved the mass of soldiery for itself and with no afterthought. I had no wish to lead them or to bellow my commands. I merely wanted to be of them, to share their dangers and their glories.

We drilled with muskets of a sort, correctly, and, apart from an occasional smirk – 'Take that grin off your face, Private Belinda!' – conscientiously. It was all so primal. We had everything to learn, Lucretia, Belinda, Milly, Sue, Tim and I. Sue and Tim were the children of a General who lived at the bottom of the hill. Lucretia and Belinda were our sisters. The posts went: Roland, Colonel; Lucretia, Sergeant; Milly (the French governess), bugler; and we four youngest, rank and file. We learnt, like Tommy Atkins in the topical song of that name, 'how to walk and where to put your feet'. The chorus went:

'Oh, Tommy Tommy Atkins, you're a good 'un heart and hand;
You're a credit to your calling and to all your native land;
May your luck be never failing may your love be ever true;
God bless you Tommy Atkins here's your Country's love to you.'

The tune wasn't much more distinguished than the words, which we knew weren't by Kipling, but, perhaps thanks to him, there was an emotion about the Army at the turn of the century that had spread far in England, and we welcomed it. The Navy could always depend on the nation's love, but affection for the Army had had to be nurtured, and South Africa at that time supplied the tilth.

Songs of parting moved us most deeply; especially the one that began: 'You are going far away, far away from poor Jeannette'; mainly because of its sweet, wailing tune. Another was the very slightly less dolorous one:

'Give my love to Nancy, she's the girl that I adore. Tell her that she'll never see her sweetheart any more. Say I died in battle, fighting 'gainst the Black. . . .' 'Gainst the Black sounded terrible.

Boastful songs we sang, like: 'Lord Roberts and Kitchener, General Buller and White: all jolly good soldiers, all ready to fight. And when we get Kruger, how happy we'll be. We'll shut him up in old England and never let him go free', to a very gay tune.

I don't think Roland knew how much I loved the generals whose coloured photographs filled a picturebook of his. He, of course, worshipped them, with their grey or white moustaches and their uniforms, sashes and medals; but, being five years younger than he was, at seven or eight years old I could hardly be supposed to rank as more than a gaping acolyte to his hierophancy.

Oh you glorious generals! There must have been forty of you in your bright bravery. You pass over now in review. Accusing or approving? Your strong faces show no emotion. Were you all as bright and brave as you looked? No boobies among you? What does it matter now? You gave us your inspiration once.

Methuen, Hector Macdonald (who, we said, killed himself because, forsooth, he was scorned for having risen from the ranks), Wauchope (of the bony cheeks), Gatacre (of Gatacre), Hunter, Dundonald, Kelly-Kenny, Smith-Dorrien, Pole-Carew, Penn-Symons, Forestier-Walker, Bindon Blood, and all you other commanders, who led or followed the 'fifty thousand horse and foot going to Table Bay'. Skinner's Horse, Strathcona's Horse, Thorneycroft's Mounted Infantry. Steady, the Buffs! Riflemen, form! All drawn up on the parade-ground of our minds. How well we knew you all!

In that South African War, waged from autumn 1899 to summer 1902, the British Field Force lost fewer than 8,000 men, leaving a few more thousand hearts in England to get over the loss as best they might. Kipling personalized it starkly:

'Soldier, soldier, come from the wars,
Did aught take 'arm to my true love?
I couldn't see the fight, for the smoke it lay so white —
An' you'd best go look for a new love.'

There was one who died in fiction whom we mourned as a brother. He was Henry Desmond, of Beauregard's Horse, in Vachell's book *The Hill*. When Roland read us the last pages, containing that letter from the veldt written the night before the battle, we could imagine no more moving experience in life or literature. Of women and horses we knew little, but of patriotism and comradely love, of uprightness, of courage in face of a pitiless foe, we thought we were competent judges. And with what artful expression did Roland read this passage!

To the friend of Desmond's bosom, still at Harrow School and doubtful of his pure and constant love, the immortal letter began:

'I have been intending to write to you, dear old chap, ever since we parted; but somehow I couldn't bring myself to tackle it in earnest till tonight. Tomorrow we have a thundering big job ahead of us; the last job, perhaps for me. Old Jonathan, you have been the best friend a man ever had, the only one I love as much as my own brothers – *and even more*!' (Could there be sweeter wine than this for sentimental heads? Nobler stuff follows.)

'It was from knowing you that I came to see what good-for-nothing fools some fellows are. You were always so unselfish and *straight* . . .'

And then . . . 'Good night, Jonathan. I'm going to turn in.' (Oh, to be big enough to 'turn in' instead of pattering upstairs to bed.) 'We shall be astir before daybreak. . . . It's so light, that I can just make out the hill upon which, I hope, our flag will be waving within a few hours . . . I have the absurd conviction strong in me that, tomorrow, I shall get up the hill here faster and easier than the other fellows because you and I have so often run up our Hill together – God bless it – and you! Good night.'

Here Roland's voice would break and I thought my heart would too. It stood the strain; but marked upon it was the resolve one day to clasp to it just such a hero-friend as Jonathan's.

As the Headmaster said in his sermon: 'To die young, clean, ardent; to die swiftly, in perfect health; to die saving others from death, or worse – disgrace; to die scaling heights . . . is not that cause for joy rather than sorrow? I say – yes.'

Scaling heights! To gaze upon far heights, heights clear or heights obscure; and then to *scale* them! I would strive to be not a mere climber but a scaler. With a comrade at my side, to what heights could I not venture? Or, if to be a hero myself were aiming too high, if I could not die leading my devoted regiment, next best would be to be loved by a hero: not like shameless Lady Hamilton, but like pure Jonathan in *The Hill*.

There was also a certain gramophone record. On the first side of it was 'The Departure of the Troopship': bands playing, crowds cheering, songs, jokes, snatches of God-speeds, and then the ship with its gallant freight moving from the shore; fainter and fainter the songs and the voices. And immediately to the other side of the record: 'The Sinking of the Troopship'. What she struck we never knew. No one let on. Submarines were not the peril, if even yet invented. Surely a rock. Drunken helmsman? We never wondered. We only heard, through the great convolvulus horn of our machine, that the good ship, which a minute before had been safe in harbour, the scene of many a loving embrace, the repository of the hopes of thousands, was sinking fast, and as like as not with all hands. Save Our Souls. Were there enough life-boats? Did they stick in the davits? What courage, as the voices rose and fell and the band played on – which heartening air is now forgotten: a favourite hymn, no doubt – while she settled lower and lower for her final plunge to the bottom.

Webland's reverie moves on to schooldays.

6

The first boarding-school, following Roland who had gone on to the second one, taught military drill. At ten years of age one was judged old enough to handle real small-arms that could fire 'rounds'. With their polygonal barrels and Martini breech action one soon learnt to move them smartly hither and yon, heavy though they felt. With a hoist here and a cant there we were soon sloping and presenting much as the London soldiers did. Of course I knew it all before; only I had never done these things in unison with more than four others, half of them female.

Sergeant Lilley could do what he liked with us, eighty strong. He was better, really, than Roland, for he wore a dark-blue uniform with golden chevrons and a row of campaign medals earned in India and Africa, fighting 'gainst the White as well as the Black; nor was he ever rude or angry. His personal abuse went no farther than occasionally to refer to us as 'The Royal Standbacks'.

With such vastly increased forces we could do more important drill. 'Forming fours' the K.R.A. could always manage, or at least 'forming four'; but it would have looked pretty thin trying to form the British Square. This we did splendidly in the school field with Sergeant Lilley in the centre. The order 'Prepare to Receive Cavalry!' thrilled and shaped us in double quick time into an inexpugnable mass of steel and flame; those in front kneeling with upstuck rifles slanted from the ground like a kind of *chevaux de frise* – but with imaginary bayonets only – and those behind standing, rifle to shoulder, as they must have done at Waterloo.

Another movement was breaking apart from close into extended order at a sign, not a word, from the Sergeant. That means that the enemy's guns are getting at you and the plump target must be denied him instantly. So we speed apart in line, some paces from one another, and flop to the earth, rifles fidgeting to speak at the word of command. 'Fire!' Five rounds rapid; then a volley from the exiguous blank cartridges. The enemy's halted. He's turning away. The extended riflemen lie tense for the word to go. Wait for it. Remember Wellington. 'Stand up, Guards!' 'Now, Maitland, now's your chance!' Watch Sergeant Lilley. Does he feel the ghost of a front-line heartbeat as he shouts the order 'Charge'? Up and away then, yelling, waving rifles, a hundred yards to the fence at the sea-cliff's edge, where we stand panting, jostling, laughing, victorious; all mock passion spent.

Another, but more peaceful, rifle exercise was very welcome to our hands and ears. Sergeant Lilley called it 'feudage war', the French *'feu de joie'*: a rippling rattle of shots fired at the sky in rapid sequence from one end of the line to the other: purely ceremonial, but, however solemn the occasion, fire of joy indeed.

In the late summer of 1914 came mobilization for real war. Roland, almost insane with patriotism, got to it less than a year before it ended. He lost his temper in the filth and danger; gained nothing material: no wound, medal, mention or promotion; and came home, just twenty years old, changed for ever.

After six months in the trenches he had written: 'For the first time now I've had enough war. All the other officers have only done one, two or three shows, but I've done four, *et j'en ai eu assez, enfin*. Oh for London again! If they leave us to rest for a few days I shall be better soon. Talk about self-control, acting; in the last show myself was non-existent and I was acting, acting the whole time to save my going off it. Heavens! how one realizes that there is a God out here, and how one prays; and what satisfaction and renewed courage after it.'

Poor Roland had the will but not the nerves of a fellow, older Guards Officer, a winner of the Victoria Cross, who was moved to write home, after fighting for seven days on end: 'It is very beautiful.'

War over, Roland's beliefs turned inside out. He blamed everyone for the sickness of the world, chiefly his parents' generation for the betrayal of youth. So the ex-Colonel of the crack Amberdines became a pacifist. Drums and flags were the devil's playthings, he said; and he preached his new faith in Hyde Park to such as cared to listen to a wild-eyed young gentleman with a histrionic style.

Still unable to sleep, Webland tries to sort out the tangles of adolescent creeds that Roland had so recklessly disturbed.

For me in a public-school Officers' Training Corps, putteed, belted, scabbarded, frogged and pouched, the old pleasure in drill soon began to wane. The rifles, very heavy to manipulate, were for men, and the rough uniform in midsummer chafed uncomfortably. Two things only retained the power to thrill: the command, 'Fix! – Bayonets!' dramatic in sound, sight and feel; and battalion parade when marching off, bayonet-tipped rifles at the slope, to the beat of the full brass band. Then something of the old pride crept back.

But mostly militarism was to be mocked. Ragging the Corps was the fashion; so that when the boy-Sergeant inspecting the line asked sharply of the boy-Private lacking some piece of equipment on his uniform: 'Why aren't you wearing a pouch?' the pert reply: 'Because I'm not a marsupial' raised the desired titter from his comrades, without endangering too much his own liberty. To such heights did courage aspire in the earliest post-war days at school.

So, by the time young manhood was reached, nothing on the mind's surface of military profit seems to have remained: nothing but the second nature that forbade one ever to step off with other than the left foot, or ever to feel right in making a left about turn. And what was the use of that? All the play-acting and the freshness and the romance and the glad discipline of a young lifetime were as a tale that is told, if not by an idiot, certainly by a bore. Farewell to arms! Hail, industry and commerce!

There would be no more war. There could be no more war. Some said that those who had fought would never fight again. Some women said that the women would never allow it. Moreover, the nations had sworn and signed, as solemnly as any bride and bridegroom in a church, that they would live, if not in amity, at least without ever being faithless or taking hostile action against one another. They were sure it would work. The cleverest men and women said that any nation that broke its word now would forfeit the respect of the others, and that moral censure alone would be enough to bring that errant one to heel; and if it improbably did not, then commercial pressure would do what verbal scolding couldn't. Permanent peace was thus assured, and now the sanest action must be to disarm the forces, if possible with others, if necessary alone.

Then there was always the puzzle of the Englishman's motto: 'For God, King, and Country!' One must make up one's mind which. All very good so long as all three are on the same tack. But what if they aren't? Then it would be as purposeless as to say: 'For Sun, Moon and Stars!' or even: 'For Home, Wife and Mistress!' There might come a moment when you'd have to decide which to put first. Was God's cause, if you could be sure which it was, always your country's? It had better be. But who was to say? The Prime Minister? The Archbishop? The Press? And what about the many Kings of England, who seemed too bad for their country and had to be removed? France clung to as wobbly a threefold national aim in her 'Liberty, Equality and Fraternity', if less manifestly untrue than the words in the American Declaration of Independence proclaiming it as self-evident that all men were created equal. No wonder the nations furiously rage when led by such rash persuasions. One could but hope that these national vapourings would never come to solid issue.

Too soon they did. Fight once more, then, for our preservation, professedly as once for Belgium, so now for Poland, and the sanctity of treaties.

But now the circumstances are different. In 1914 they wanted volunteers; they called, they wrote, they drew, they sang for volunteers, so desperately needed to expand the slim Expeditionary Force on the Continent. Not to respond to your country's call was to be a shirker of the basest kind, and a coward to boot. Only after nearly

two years, when the flowers had all been picked, was
conscription of the weeds daringly introduced. But in
this second war, more or less in contravention of a
Government pledge, conscription was decreed some
months before the war broke out.

*Beginning to get sleepy now, Webland rehearses the problem of
national service.*

What was wanted of the likes of me? 'It all depends on
me,' they said; or did they say 'you'? Where was the front
now? This war wouldn't be won by service-men alone,
but by men and women on four or five fronts: military,
industrial and mercantile, agricultural and civil defence.

What is an unconditioned company director of middle-
age rightly to do? Push into the armed forces unrequired?
'Is this a private war?' say the wags; 'or can anyone join in?'
The Whitehall people know what they want and whom
they can absorb. They'll send for you when they need you.
Let it be Civil Defence then, for the time being, and await
the call-up. Anything may happen in this war of aeroplanes.
Poison gas may be used, bacteria too, and the enemy may
drop from gliders by night, disguised as females, holy or
unholy, in a convention of descending nuns or a flutter
of strumpets, their underclothes stuffed with weapons.

At the fall of France a greater wave of patriotism swept
the country. Not only adventurous bachelors and disil-
lusioned husbands flocked, as one used to say, to the
colours, in search of a cause and a purpose in their rootless
lives; but staid citizens, mindful of what their fathers and
brothers had done in that earlier war, couldn't bear to stay
at home any longer and were boiling to do the same. Former schoolfellows, fit or fat, clamoured for acceptance as
officers in the Brigade of Guards, and presumably on the
strength of a certificate of proficiency lightly gained
twenty years before in the O.T.C. they were in and on
parade almost before you could say 'As you were'. Even
Roland was in uniform again.

But what of us who had not bothered to gain this certificate? What right had we to be commissioned in the

smartest regiments of Britain? Could one get in by
influence? Here and there it looked like it. There was old
Henry Rank-Boyson, for instance, who had certainly been
dismissed with ignominy from the school Corps; bald and
corpulent, he got in. How? Hadn't his uncle once commanded one of the regiments?

All right, Webland. You wait till you are sent for. That
will be your proper time. Meanwhile, carry on, civilian.
Work, watch and defend. This is no volunteer's war
as it was in Roland's day; and remember that ten – or
is it twenty or thirty? – civilians and back-area soldiers
are now needed for every one in the fighting-line. Don't
get over-excited and lose your wits to claptrap sentiment.
Remember what the schoolmaster said to the Hill boys
about the South African War: 'There has been too much
cheap excitement.'

Yet the pull was strong. Twenty years of cobwebs
swept off the soul, and the mute call to arms, if irrational,
was insistent. Why not hand this Air Raid Precautions
Control, this training and practising and night-watching
on to someone older, and be off to the Recruiting Office?
Not without a word, though, like a runaway schoolboy.
Talk to the Chief; explain to him that most of the training
and organizing are now in good shape and that this rural
district is no place for an old K.R.A. man to abide in.

But the Chief forcefully pleaded his greater need and
said that he would seek powers to retain the services of
his second-in-command. He had been a Colonel long ago
and the military phrases came easily.

He said that he hoped I would attach as much weight to
his views as I did to my own personal wishes; that our
organization might soon be put to severe tests and that it
was essential that men occupying responsible positions
should remain; that my departure would throw much
extra work on his shoulders and that it would be quite
impossible to replace me. 'Very well then, Colonel, I'll
stay.' 'Good man!' 'But when my turn comes in the conscription list, off I go.' 'Well, we'll see about that.'

Months passed. 'IF THE INVADER COMES', said the Ministry of Information pamphlet, 'the ordinary men and women of the civilian population will also have their part to play. . . . *You must not be taken by surprise.* . . . Follow three rules: (1) If the Germans come, by parachute, aeroplane or ship, you must remain where you are. The order is "STAY PUT". (2) Do not believe rumours and do not spread them. . . . If in doubt ask the policeman or the A.R.P. Warden.' (God help us! That's P.C. Stoat and Mrs Barnowl.) '(3) Keep watch. If you see anything suspicious, note it carefully and go at once to the nearest police officer. . . . Do not rush about spreading vague rumours. . . .'

A few bombs fell in the area. A field of hops was blown to dust. Autumn, winter, and another spring went by. But we can't 'stay put' like this: talking, writing, watching, practising for nothing to come. Invasion is out of the question now.

Old General Despard, controlling the adjoining A.R.P. area, after a visit of inspection and discussion, said:

'You seem to be doing single-handed what most Controllers employ two or three assistants and a whole-time clerk to do.'

'That's because there's hardly any more work to do here. I shall be called up any day now and I've decided that I shall do better in the ranks of the Royal Air Force.'

'Good Heavens, man; now that the war demands the proper use of manpower it's perfectly absurd that you, with your knowledge and organizing ability, should waste time in the lower ranks of the R.A.F.'

'Oh, I shall put in for a commission as soon as I can. My friend, Frank Mead, who is a Flight-Lieutenant at a Fighter Station, has written to say that he's asking for me to join him.'

But a friend in the Government which had introduced the conscription, hearing of this decision, wrote: 'For goodness' sake don't go and get caught up in the machinery.' No doubt he knew the entanglement of it; but it is

13

exactly this new machinery that has to be worked. We shall see. Entry through the ranks is good and should be encouraged, not avoided. Higher and lower are losing touch again. Having become once more part of the human mass, how profitable then to rise from the ranks with a new understanding and a surer command.

Carlyle wrote, on what he called the Unworking Authority: 'Descend, O Donothing Pomp; quit thy down-cushions; expose thyself to learn what wretches feel, and how to cure it! The Czar of Russia became a dusty toiling shipwright; worked with his axe in the Docks of Saardam; and his aim was small to thine.' Obviously Carlyle would be all for putting Railway Directors into the ranks.

Preliminary papers in July led to an interview with an elderly Officer in the county town. 'A past Works Manager and a present Director of several large companies? Oh yes; Special Duties for you.'

Special, by jingo! No commonplace duties. That can mean nothing less than high Intelligence or deep Espionage work. Excellent. I'll not betray their trust in me at this time, and England shall ne'er have cause to rue. . . . How does the quotation go?

At last the call-up came; late enough. Why hadn't they sent for me before? Had the Chief anything to do with the delay? He said at parting:

'The initiative which you've shown in bringing our organization up to what I feel is a very high standard of efficiency has been invaluable. I'm sure you appreciate the very great amount which I personally relied upon you to support me. We all wish you success in your new venture, and hope that very soon you will be doing a class of work in which your outstanding ability will be recognized.'

The Chief, looking now oddly like Sir Hector Macdonald, seemed to raise his voice rather unnecessarily, as he added: 'You are sure to *rise and shine* . . .'

'RISE AND SHINE! WAKEY WAKEY!'

Webland awakes in amazement.

14

2
Not Yet Diagnosed

'Now, Mr Tapley,' said Mark, giving himself a
tremendous blow in the chest by way of a reviver,
'just you attend to what I've got to say. Things is
looking about as bad as they *can* look, young man.
You'll not have such another opportunity for
showing your jolly disposition, my fine fellow,
as long as you live.'

CHARLES DICKENS – *Martin Chuzzlewit*

Enters a stamping Sergeant: 'Come on out of it there,
sharp!' and thunders off to the other rooms.

'Cheer up, chum,' says a voice, 'the first five years are
the worst.' It's come at last. This is no dream. In fact, it's
the first minute of the first hour of the first morning.
They won't be here long, though, because this is only
an assembly place for recruits: someone's seaside board-
ing-house in peacetime, now thoroughly defurnished for
the brief lodgement of civilians to be clad as airmen and
sent in batches about the kingdom to be broken in.

There are ten rooms in this building for about fifty
men, two water-closets, two wash-basins, and no hot
water. The place is Glanville, the month is September,
the time is 5.30 a.m., and the weather is good.

Yesterday, on arrival, an inhospitable-looking Corporal, neither spick nor span, had received the men as
they arrived in their civilian clothes with their small
suitcases. He had taken them to eat a meal of salt beef and
rice, with nothing to drink. Thence to the doctor, or the

15

Medical Officer, or the M.O. They must accustom themselves to using initials now.

Inspection by the M.O. is very important. Some of the men may be unclean. Up with their shirts and down with their trousers, to be peered at behind an electric torch aimed at crops of hair on the body. They must accustom themselves to it, so that there shall be no surprise in these first few days when any spare half-hour may be used for being shone upon by the medical torch. What are M.O.s looking for, and whatever do they find? Webland fears he may never know. He wants to learn much. With the goal of a commission before him, he will do everything yarely and try to be the smartest airman that ever bashed a square; which, he has already learnt, is R.A.F. slang for recruit-drill. There must be no slacking, shirking, scrounging or belly-aching.

The torch moved on to other parts and Webland had passed his first test. They marched – no more walking; all marching now – to tea at 3.45, and that was the last meal of the day. It was a ponderous cold meat pasty, bread, margarine, jam, yellow cake and strange-tasting tea, probably chlorinated. So soon after the midday meal why did they give one another, and then nothing more for fifteen hours? Presumably it had been carefully worked out by dieticians. But it startled the new airmen to be expected to subsist so long and so soon upon air.

Then, suddenly, there was nothing to do. The spectre of boredom was taking shape already. What should one do? Webland went down to the shore and stared at the sea for a few hours, then went to bed. The evening sounds were a wireless jazzband, boots on stairs, laughter, whistling, and croon-singing; the smells, cigarette smoke and disinfectant.

At 9.30 the air-raid sirens had wailed, the lights had gone out, his five room-mates had come in and stumbled noisily into bed: blankets over three two-foot square mattresses stuffed with straw, known as biscuits.

This morning the room-mates are already on easy

16

terms: a Scotch lad, a Midlands lad, and three Welshmen of more nearly middle age.

Now for the morning's events. Breakfast: a piece of bacon overwhelmed by saucy baked beans; also bread and tea. Webland eats it easily, but a small, sharp Cockney recruit refers to the beans with such disgusting imagery that Webland resolves never again to make jokes about food.

They are marched off to be kitted, put into uniform. Here's a surprise. In the pocket of his tunic is a note, reading: 'If you want a pen-pal write to Miss Eunice Hipcraft, 1284 Side Street, Swindon.' Well, that's friendly; astute, too, in such a friendless hour. A pen-pal. But what rocks might such a palship strike? No; this plutonic friendship is not for Webland.

Hats (steel and service), jackets, overcoats, shirts, trousers, till the set's complete: all in a white kit-bag. The lads are in uniform now, looking at one another in mock admiration. Webland is told he looks very smart and well-fitted. But where is his civilian gas-mask that has to be slung across his shoulder in its cubic cardboard box? He must have left it at home. This is a bad start. He is the only one without it. Shall he ask the Corporal, already testy after months of pastoral work among dull recruits? Or will the answer be: 'If I hear one more bloody word about your . . .'? Better say nothing. The boots are stiff round the lower shins; otherwise the costume is roughly comfortable.

Groups of men are divided into Flights. Ambiguous noun. Verb: to fly or to flee. This lot looks more fit for the latter. Webland is in C Flight. He must remember that: easier to remember than his precious number, which is seven digits ending with 107. That termination is important, for henceforward it is the indispensable indentification of Aircraftman (not Aircraftsman) Webland, 4121107, or 107 for short.

Ranks are formed: not in two lines, as in the old O.T.C., but in three. No more forming fours. That was abolished years ago. Something new to learn. No one seems keen, but it's hardly fair to judge yet, this place being only an enlistment depot. There is little discipline today and plenty of chat in the ranks. Webland avoids being placed next to a surly-looking would-be mutineer and succeeds in getting beside a mild solicitor, who confides that military service loses him all his salary and that he will have only the daily half-crown plus wife allowance; but he doesn't complain. One of the men says: 'Oh well, we must make the best of it. That's the only thing to do. But it's the wife and kids I'm sorry for.' Kids? Webland has a wife and kids, and, while on the subject of young goats, a nanny, too, to pay, and certain servants. He'll be poorer, but his household can manage.

One of the first marches is to the padre, who gives the Flight some practical advice, both negative and positive. He says you should not put your best girl in the family way, but should rub your feet with methylated spirit, and soap the inside of your socks. The solicitor wants to know afterwards if the whole world is mad, with twenty million servicemen putting soap in their socks for Hitler. That's nothing to what else they'll find themselves doing.

Meanwhile fraternization proceeds. Webland has already been offered tobacco, biscuit, apple and toffee. How generous are the poor in pocket, and what a part is played in their lives by treats of food! Much can be learnt at a certain eating place where the troops forgather when duty's done. It is called the NAAFI: the Naffy.

He starts to get acquainted with his issued equipment. Someone must help him to analyse this smallest inhabitant of his kit-bag, termed a housewife and pronounced a huzzif. Inside it are needles and thimble and suchlike. It radiates domestic confidence. Another delectable present is a set of what are called 'irons', meaning a knife, spoon, and fork, which, wrapped in a duster and seconded by an enamel mug, accompany each man to his meals: so much more hygienic than the common-mouth utensils of civilization. Why hasn't everyone always brought his own irons to restaurants, in silver or gold if he likes?

Now all civilian clothes are packed up in suitcases, locked, and handed to the Sergeant to send to the men's homes. The keys follow by personal envelope. Those who have no suitcases are able to procure brown paper and string from a Corporal sitting at a table. One of Webland's new Welsh friends asks for two pieces of paper and some string.

'That'll be ninepence from you,' says the Corporal.

'What's that for?' says Jenkins.

'Threepence the string; threepence each piece of paper.'

'I'm not going to pay that. I thought we'd come here to be paid.'

'Take it or leave it.'

'I'll pay you if you'll write me out a receipt.'

This is a shrewd request, but the Corporal is also shrewd and stands firm. He is in a strong position, with the goods and his experience behind him and a one-day-old recruit before him. The queue and the Corporal are becoming impatient, and Jenkins pays. So do they all.

'Good-bye, Civvy Street,' say the men. What an urban country is ours: we are not so much Shakespeare's 'hempen home-spuns' and 'rude mechanicals' as Kipling's 'street-bred people'. Webland's clothes go back to no Civvy Street but to a Civvy Hillside in the green peace of Civvyshire. The kit-bag is now his trunk, wardrobe, hangers and shelves, and to dress and undress from is another craft that must be practised.

Every man receives ten shillings this day, the basis of which pay is not yet understood. Very soon, perhaps tomorrow, the Flight will be sent to its place of training for square-bashing. Spirits rise a little, and friendships are beginning to form. Tolerance is shown to the few tiresome ones, and Webland's Welsh room-mates are already proving their more joyous sense of humour. One is a grocer, one an insurance agent and the third a tombstone-maker. As he had hoped, he finds himself at ease in their company; and, as he sits on the wires of his iron bed learning to sew on his first flown button and absorbing the quasi-military atmosphere, he experiences his first adult emotion of sharing with fellow sufferers an unwelcome life in perfect equality under crushing authority. This is the beginning of comradeship.

One of the Welshmen cannot yet satisfy Webland's new desire for social equality. Although he is nearly of the same age, his natural courtesy and our British class system, based upon relative wealth and lineage, compel him to call his English mate with the B.B.C. accent 'Mister Webland'. This won't do.

'You don't want to go on calling me Mr Webland. Call me Webland or any name you like.'

'Well, you see,' says Jenkins, 'you are my superior.'

'I'm not your superior. We're all equal: all of us; right down at the bottom.'

'Righto, Mister Webland.'

'Oh, Mr Jenkins, you do disappoint me.'

There is a reason for this difficulty, and he had wondered from the beginning how it would operate. Before this war those entering the ranks of the Services had been almost always youths, often ill-educated and of poor estate. On that fact had been based the regulations, customs and standardized treatment of the mass of rough recruits. Webland, with many others, was neither young nor rough. He was approaching forty, was short-sighted and not jolly in horseplay. Moreover, he had been reared in a masters' world of subordinates and dependants. The custom was so ancient that it seemed natural. Now had come a time for adjustment.

His case, however, possessed a feature that made it rather more unusual. His father, still alive, had many years before occupied a position of national importance, but in his retirement had fallen into disfavour with the Press and the public. The Services, as the armed embodiment of patriotism, felt especially aggrieved towards this once popular figure; and none more so, as it happened, than the Royal Air Force. Hence Webland's apprehension.

It was scarcely possible, even had it been desirable, for him to conceal his close relationship to the celebrated Montagu Webland, now Lord Webland, and he had come to the decision at his first contact with the Service to take it in his military stride and hope for the best. Indeed, there was no other way. Consequently it was not long before those around him had become aware of his situation; but he was relieved to observe that they were taking him as they saw him and letting their judgement bide the future.

There were some curious fish in the conscription draft net. If a man could walk and understand most of what was said to him it seems that he was accepted. The recruits had evidently been pricked or not for service somewhat as King Henry's soldiers had. Falstaff: 'Well said, courageous Feeble! Thou wilt be as valiant as the wrathful dove or most magnanimous mouse. Prick the woman's tailor well, Master Shallow; deep, Master Shallow.'

In Webland's Flight of a hundred and sixty there was a tradesman who was too fat to be fitted into any uniform. Poor fellow, he puffed his way through the drill wearing conspicuous civvies for a long time, but he fined down a bit and remained in the race.

Another was said to be a criminal and presumably would take some forcing into shape. He looked as though he might not respond to treatment.

Another, misshapen and drowsy, was plainly unable to comprehend why he was there, and before long, in pity or despair, he was taken away and restored to his friends and relations.

A fourth was so small that the smallest uniform almost eclipsed him. He was allowed, however, to wear his own civilian shoes, because size 3 was not issued in boots for the forces. Well for him that he wore them for, whenever the Flight marched, he, submerged in the middle, ran tirelessly with it, although he was said to be half paralysed. Webland's Welsh friends were too kind-hearted to mock him within sight or hearing, but the situation suited their extravagant national humour and the speculation in the billets after dark upon the details of Tich's private past and public future were outrageous in their ingenuity. It wasn't long before he was taken out of the ranks of giants and appointed to be a kind of Flight birdsbody, to do no drill but to trot round with messages for N.C.O.s. There he found his *métier*, for he was merry-hearted and could always contribute a grin and often a dirty repartee. He left before the course began and was much missed, if only as a cheerfully bewildered mascot.

Another day is started with a breakfast of smashed fish out of cans, washed down by thick tea which the men suppose to be made with sea-water. To Webland, who is no connoisseur of either but only has a good appetite, all food comes alike, and he is even able to eat some rejected by one of his neighbours. He no longer minds the crooning and the radio that booms day and night from the Sergeant's room.

While waiting to be posted to the square-bashing camp he and his fellows are a species of nothing: neither civilians nor airmen. There is a certain comfort in being the lowest of the low and in knowing that there can scarcely be any further declension. No burden of responsibility weighs down the mind; furthermore, something must happen soon.

It does, on the fourth day. The Corporal perpetrates the well-worn military witticism: 'I want four volunteers. You, you, you and you!' Four of the larger men are picked, Webland among them, and are bidden to fetch spades and proceed to a near-by aerodrome. A lorry drive is a treat, even if it means shovelling two tons of wet sand into it, sitting on it for the drive back and shovelling it out again into a shed, after first clearing the place of its decayed rubbish and bottles. Here Webland is given his first command in charge of the work, for the Corporal asks what the four men's occupations had been: two clerks, a bank cashier and – what should Webland confess to? He had had several occupations. Works Manager had been one of them, and on that profession he was ordered to control the operation.

'Never volunteer,' say the old soldiers, 'and never let on that you know anything.' But Webland disagrees. No advancement can come from never putting yourself forward.

Drenched with sweat, prickled by sand and clothing, when the job is finished he finds the public baths by the pier, and for fourpence he lies down in the first warm water since he left home. Complete enjoyment is diminished by having to get back into his wet and smelly shirt, and by finding flea-bites, perhaps from that shovelled sand, on his chest.

One of the men says: 'The things I do for England!' That sand was a job well done, and the poet says all service ranks the same with God, so Webland is not dismayed when the order comes to scrub the floor of the bedroom with that whitish liquid sometimes seen in public lavatories and on underground railway platforms. There is clearly a certain skill to be attained in scrubbing floors. No doubt there will be further practice at the next place, for word goes round that the Flight is to leave in the morning for wherever it may be, accompanied by a warning to expect rough treatment there.

Four crude days and nights have taught him to call up new powers of body and spirit, and he feels ready for anything. In this newly discovered comradeship there is no hardship that cannot be positively enjoyed. He is keen as a young man once more to get on and to help his country too. It is almost like being back with Roland and the K.R.A.

For all the relative squalor of the first days of service there is no real cause for worry. One matter, though, does slightly trouble him. The Corporal, who had received the draft, in the last hour had passed his hat round for coins of gratitude, which most of the dazed recruits were in no state to question; so the man did well out of it. First, the insidious paper and string; now this. Where can the Officer be?

The assorted airmen of C Flight, mates of five days' standing – so much of them standing – rise on the morning of departure at the usual hour of five-thirty, march the three-quarters of a mile to breakfast, parade again at eight-fifteen with kit-bags replete, rations and water-bottles ditto. Packing the kit-bag has to be geometrical and muscular, what with a greatcoat and a steel hat, in addition to the total issued equipment. It is done at last and, by planning and rearranging and some jumping upon, its mouth roped shut and padlocked. With the three-foot long 60 lb. hard and soft canvas sausage on the shoulder, head bent sideways, they march the two or three hundred yards to Glanville railway station. In heaving his kit-bag up, Webland, unpractised yet, brings the hard side of it into sharp collision with his ear. This sly act of revenge on the part of his gagged and over-stuffed fellow-traveller draws first blood and annoys him unreasonably. He paraphrases Swinburne's petulant line about roses: 'I shall never be friends again with kit-bags'; and feels for a moment quite abominably ill-used.

Throughout the journey there is roll-calling by Sergeants and Corporals. 'One O Seven Webland!' is roared. 'Sergeant!' is roared back. Roaring is *à la mode* on parade. Webland knows all about this and can roar louder than most. Twenty minutes of standing in line outside the station; twenty minutes of the same on the platform; then in comes the train. Troops dash for compartments so as to be in the same one as each's particular pal. Webland, long taught to make way for others, is in last. A Warrant Officer, the highest rank yet closely encountered, appears, roaring: 'Come on; get in there! For God's sake, watcher waitin' for?' expecting no answer from God or man. Ten minutes in that train; all change at a junction; forty minutes of waiting on the platform; then the rush again,

into the train-corridor, wrestling with kit-bags, finding
compartments filled and filling with blue-clad airmen.
Webland gets a seat at last among a group of youths who
plainly don't want him, being bent upon keeping places
for their friends. Luckily Jenkins follows him in. Webland
finds the piece of paper in his pocket from Miss Hipcraft
and passes it on to the youths, who are delighted. The
atmosphere of unwelcome is quite dispelled.

In two or three hours the train stops at Cadstone-on-
Sea. Out they scramble, across the road into a large
building, to be welcomed in service fashion by fifteen to
twenty scowling Royal Air Force N.C.O.s swearing
fiercely among themselves as they prepare to roar the
roll-call. Slowly the mass is formed into Squads and
marched off to billets a mile away on the sea-front. It is
late afternoon, the weather's fine and the sea blue; but
the kit-bag leans heavy now on arm, shoulders and mal-
treated ear.

Webland's Squad of twenty-seven men lines up outside
a small private hotel, the Cliffhaven; the Corporal selects
four men of what he takes to be more refined aspect, and
the rest march off to another building. Webland, among
the select, is asked if he has a pal. The only answer to be
made is 'No, Corporal'; the consequence of which is that
he is shown into a little room with one bed in it all to
himself. Here's luck. Can it last?

It is good to be lodged in seaside boarding-houses
instead of the expected camp huts; and it is good to eat
the evening meal – is it tea or supper? – where the main
Squad is billeted in a house near-by at five separate tables
in what was once an elegant parlour. Both billets belong
to a stern landlord, called Mr Procket, who lives in the
same building in which Webland and his three clean comrades are privileged to be quartered. There are also in the
Cliffhaven three or four elderly civil servants engaged on
their various war-works. Nothing, in the circumstances,
could be more pleasant. A hard bed and pillow give no
cause for complaint after the past nights of straw, and

how can one complain of constant cold water if one can sometimes beg from the landlord a jug of hot? But to be alone at night is a blessing beyond all padres'.

Parade is at eight-thirty in the morning: steady slogging at elementary drill in Squads, interspersed with lectures. Muscles are loosening, stiff boots less stiff, and Webland's spirits are rising with the exercise and the prospect of six short weeks of technical improvement. This at last, he feels, is what his once thought wasted years of drill have trained him for.

He wonders about the medical trouser and torch drill and if the authorities have forgotten to peep in to see how everything is getting on beneath the uniform; for they've been at Cadstone now nearly twenty-four hours. At four o'clock comes a lecture to five hundred of them by a fleshy young R.A.F. doctor of Levantine aspect. He gives, from the stage of a concert-hall, a racy talk on the care of the body, and what to do about women. It may not be intended to be coarse, but the lecturer is perhaps in search of popularity, and the scanty laughs that he raises are not whole-hearted. He offends the taste of some, not so much by his assertion that there is not a virgin to be found in Cadstone and the implication that none is free from the pox, as by suggesting that in the certain event of randy airmen catching it, they will infect the wife, who will lose no time in passing it on to the boy-friend.

'Claptrap,' mutters Webland to his bewildered neighbour.

The discourse over, the troops are instructed to take off their shirts and file outside for torso investigation. Webland gets through the exit no sooner than last but one. He will have to learn to practise those little discourtesies that help so much to oil the wheels of one's own wagon. He lines up with the others, and down come five hundred pairs of trousers. All seem to pass the searching beam with blushing colours – for passers-by can observe almost as much as they please through the thin bushes that border the street – and the M.O. gives a lingering look at Webland's chest, where the flea-bites glow, as though resolved to claim at least and at last one victim.

'How long have you had that?'

'I think since yesterday, sir. It's a flea-bite.'

Inside the hall clothes are resumed, and Webland's name and one other are roared out. His mates are surprised. He holds his hand up, roars 'Here', and is told to report to the Corporal. Picked out already from half a thousand men, his is some form of distinction, though it may be only for a bottle of ointment. He is to report at the M.O.'s office. From there he is sent off to get tea and return with 'small kit' for conveyance in an ambulance to hospital.

He says: 'But, sir, I know this is a flea-bite.' (What wonderful care they take of one's health here.)

'Never mind that. We'll soon catch him for you.'

The M.O. is not one to argue with a recruit. He gives him a piece of paper on which is written '*Pediculosis. N.Y.D.*'

It is now dusk, and Webland is conveyed in the ambulance to what serves as an emergency hospital in a dimly lit building three or four miles away at Coastington. After a long wait downstairs he is given two plates, a dirty mug, an old knife, fork and spoon, and a very small pair of stained pyjamas. He is then taken to a room on the top floor occupied by two Londoners, pimpled, cropped, dyed in green and purple patches, and strangely unfriendly. He is directed to the remaining empty bed, told to touch nothing and to wait. Not having been forbidden to talk, he asks the Londoners about their state of health and is told that he is in an isolation ward for Scabies and Crabs.

A hospital orderly growls: 'Bring yer shaving things along 'ere.' Webland follows him into a bathroom where a black-out light is glowing dimly, and in the sub-twilight he is ordered to have a hot bath and to shave himself from neck to toe: everywhere except scalp and eyebrows. But why should these be excused? Since this is a matter of hair, cannot the bugs set up their quarters here as well as there? And what exactly is or are Scabies and what are or is Crabs? Answers to these questions had better not be attempted at present. A kindlier looking orderly comes in and Webland makes one more effort at freedom. He says the M.O. at Cadstone has made a mistake and that if only the doctor at the hospital would come and have a look the whole thing would be cleared up in two minutes. No; the doctor's not about now.

'Well, can I see the night doctor in private when he comes on duty?'

'I'm sorry, laddie, but you've got to shave yourself all over. If you choose to disobey orders you can; but those are my instructions.'

Disobey orders? Here's a pickle. He wonders how long this isolation is going to last, how this set-back is going to affect his training course, whether it would be prudent to begin his military career by disobeying orders in his very first week. The K.R.A. had never prepared him for a situation like this; nor had Sergeant Lilley; nor had the O.T.C. Appeal, then? Whom did one appeal to in the dark of a doctorless emergency hospital at a coastal town? Is there a telephone? Whom to ring up? A Member of Parliament? The Air Ministry? But one is not allowed to touch anything, and they wouldn't show one where the telephone is. All clothes have been taken away to be disinfected. Sneaking downstairs and out to a call-box would be madness in these child's pyjamas half-way up the legs and arms and gapped across the chest. Then would come the strait-jacket. Remember Strindberg's *The Father*. Besides, isn't this rather a small matter to start worrying over? Aren't people being blasted to death every day in this hideous war? And who is Webland to cry 'Not me!' when faced by a speck of frustration? And – preposterous thought but not impossible – what if the newspapers got to know that Montagu Webland's son, having failed, probably abetted by his shameless father, to escape conscription, had started his service by shrieking for special privileges? Some journalists would relish that

28

if short of spicier news. But this is what old Geoffrey had meant when he had warned him not to go and get caught up in the machinery. Well, he's caught up now and this is his big test. Shall he fail after six days?

So he shaves as he's never shaved before: one hour this evening and another hour at dawn; blade after blade, cut and bleed and cut and come again. In the dusk he dabs himself with a towel that doesn't feel like his own. Nor is it. Then, from a tub of grey-green grease, a smearing over the whole field of operations. He thinks he recognizes the stuff as the same that he used to rub on his dog for mange.

Outside the bathroom door he descries a label fixed. It reads 'SCABIES ONLY'. Oh, well, if he hadn't got it before, thanks to the mistaken towel he's surely got it now: Scabies *and* Crabs, a pretty pair: like constellations in the Zodiac.

In bed his thoughts won't let him sleep. The sour Londoners under their painted pimples are snoring like speed-boats; the tight pyjama jacket has stopped the circulation in his arms. He sheds it. He wonders whether his mates are missing him, even pitying him perhaps. They understand unfairness as the upper strata never can.

Morning comes, and more shaving. In the haunted bathroom the good-natured orderly gives a few blade-strokes down the unattainable small of the back. That ought to be all right. The ward is filled with cigarette smoke. The ill-natured orderly comes in with metal ash-trays and throws them at each bed. Webland's goes under the bed. He doesn't need it. 'Pick it up,' snaps the orderly. Should he give orders to me? thinks Webland. What exactly is an orderly? One who gives orders, or takes them, or both? Better obey. Webland picks it up.

He remembers it is his parents' golden wedding-day. He must send them a telegram. He asks an orderly, then a nurse, then a doctor. No one has ever done such a thing from such a place. Out of the question.

The doctor comes in to inspect bodies and tells

Webland he hasn't shaved nearly enough and he's to do it again. This is astonishing. Do these M.O.s suffer from hallucinations? Have they seen so much awry that they can't stop seeing it everywhere? Shave on, then. But the zest has gone out of the labour and the skin is beginning to smart. This isn't the kind of bloody smartness he'd intended to achieve.

The next day comes, and without further inspection he is told he is cured and is to be off, back to his Squad. Still more astonishing. How do they know without looking? Perhaps it's a three day wonder, this *Pediculosis. N.Y.D.*, and clears itself up on its own. Perhaps the doctor has had a break-down, has proclaimed a general amnesty and gone over the cliff. What matter? Webland is free and outside, hoping for a bus back to Cadstone. How he longs for his mates. He wonders how much training he's missed and whether he can make up for what he's lost. Little do the citizens of this town know that the airman they see standing at the pavement's edge has a normal head but elsewhere is utterly hairless; and little would they care if they knew. He is determined before he catches it again to discover the meaning of *Pediculosis. N.Y.D.*

Of course it is easily interpreted when he rejoins his knowledgeable friends in the Squad. It does mean Crabs after all; and N.Y.D. stands for 'Not Yet Diagnosed', which signifies that the doctor wouldn't like to promise he's right in case he's ever got at by a litigious victim. That puts him, and the Ministry, right for any diagnosis. Just as well.

3

A Marked Man

All are not soldiers that go to the wars.
Spanish Proverb

Back in his billets on Saturday Webland finds, as in some
Secret Service tale, that his possessions have disappeared:
clothes, spare boots, bed-clothes – everything; gone, he
is told, to be baked; so he has nothing clean to put on
until he can recover them. In his absence the landlord has
discovered his identity. He invites him not to take his
meals down the road in the mess-room with the others,
but with himself and a handsome instructor and ex-Life-
guardsman, Corporal Cowley, and two or three civil
servants in the dining-room, all set out with knives and
forks, napkins and glass tumblers. This invitation can
hardly be refused, and Webland finds the evident favour
doesn't upset his mates. His confidence in them and theirs
in him is already becoming established.

Meanwhile there is no time to be lost, much to make up.
Boots have to be transformed from their dull, hippo-hide
surface to a gleam like patent leather. Bone, spit, polish,
bone, spit, polish, for about an hour each day for weeks,
and then they 'come up'. The rest is comparatively easy.

Certain articles must now be bought in the town:
marking-ink for garments, a clothes-brush, boot-polish
and a cloth to rub the boots with; button-polish, stick
and rag also. So to the shops. A big Scotchman from the

31

Flight suggests they should both have a hair-cut. More hair to shed. Sixpence to a service barber renders the back and sides bristly enough for another ten days at least.

A young airman, recognizing a recruit by his civilian gas-mask, asks Webland how he is enduring the Raff. The airman says he was properly browned off when he started, but after eighteen months he was beginning to settle down. 'Browned off with the Raff!' Webland must learn this new language and have what sport he can with it. He himself is too much interested and busy to be browned off. He has his immediate goal, too, which is to do well at the six weeks' drilling, supposed to be much the worst part of service life, and to try for a commission on the strength of that and such parts of his civilian career as may seem creditable. No; he is not likely to be browned off by days of profitable training, with comrades like these to share them. He has been called 'Mate', 'Chum', 'Pal', 'Brother' – names that he has never borne before. 'Bert' he has been called, and 'Arthur', and 'George', so that in this cloud of friendliness he feels he can answer to any name, even as a dog to a whistle.

There is to be no parade for the Flight on Sunday, not even for Church, because they were all vaccinated and inoculated the day before. Webland, having missed that, must be done on the following Saturday. His mates tell him that it was like sticking cattle and that twenty-two men had fainted. You are given forty-eight hours for recovery, they say; but some it takes badly. They commiserate with him over his hospital treatment and he with them over their inoculations. They are all getting to know one another, to sort out for mutual congeniality and tentatively to pal up.

One or two ask Webland in no unfriendly fashion if his dad is still abroad, plainly prompted by a suggestion in one or two of the newspapers that Lord Webland has been comfortably situated since 1939 far from his country's danger. Although the alleged fact has been seen in print, they seem disposed to accept his assurance that it is not a fact at all and that the old man has been at home from the start.

A cockney printer, of about Webland's age but of four weeks' seniority on the recruits' course, takes a liking to him, calls him Arthur – Theodore can't be risked – and wishes to play cribbage or go for walks or to the cinema with him. He is sharp-witted and companionable, but Webland is disinclined for such diversions. The first printer Webland has been acquainted with outside of *Box and Cox*, Bob is billeted next door, but he comes often into the Cliffhaven Hotel where his good nature has made him a kind of house favourite.

A little saint of a recruit from Middlesbrough, observing Webland's despair over the shine on his boots, comes in to spend half an hour spitting and polishing them on the bedroom floor, demonstrating how to 'bring them up'. First, he rubs vehemently with a bone toothbrush handle; then he smears blacking and spit on the cloth; then he dry-brushes; then he shiny-cloth wipes. Being red-haired he is called Ginger. His father had been out of work in the shipyards for seven years, his mother is an invalid, and the R.A.F. pays his wife 25/– a week, out of which she pays 15/– a week for rent. He is an upholsterer and is always cheerful.

Walking down the road one evening after dark to help him post a letter Ginger tells Webland of the queer sort of chaps one meets, and of having a good wife 400 miles away, and – the serviceman's constant problem – of the importance of not getting led astray and being unfaithful. He finds Webland suits him champion, being also a good husband and not a dance-goer. He says one meets thousands of chaps and doesn't fancy any of them, and then one meets a chap like Webland. . . .

Men in uniform search always for a pal; the need is paramount, and there is a rush at the canteen, before a march or a bus-ride, to get near one's own particular friend. It is a craving for cosiness and affection in the harshness of this disciplined life. Mulvaney, Ortheris and

33

Learoyd felt it long ago in India, as do these recent printers and upholsterers at this south-coast town.

The friendship is soon cut short, as service friendships are, by the 'abhorred shears' of 'posting'. At 6.45 one morning Ginger gets kitted up and leaves, his six weeks up, with a warm and novel parting. He pats Webland's cheek saying: 'Keep yer chin up, Arthur.' 'Good-bye' for all its sincerity seems an unsuitably cold rejoinder and sticks in Webland's throat. 'Cheero' and 'Ta-ta' he has often heard, but not yet articulated. He chooses: 'All the best', means it, and hopes it is the best. Good-bye, Ginger! True hearted, brave, northern upholsterer. What can go wrong with England if it breeds chaps like you? Webland's chin shall be kept up, come what may.

Bob, the printer, with his warm heart, quick wit and filthy jokes remains a week longer. He uses the cockney rhyming slang. An extension by association also figures in this London language: for instance, he calls a whore a 'Brasso', which is a metal-polish. He explains how it works. 'Whore' rhymes with 'door'. Door has a handle which has to be polished. He considers Webland a queer one, but evidently likes him, and is grateful when Webland spends half an hour trying to help him to do sums with square roots. There is little that Webland can teach anyone in matters of practical and domestic craft, and he is pleased that he has contributed something at last. Perhaps he may show some knowledge of drill and so counterbalance his inadequacy as a handy man.

The weather this autumn is glorious, the preliminaries are over, and square-bashing starts in earnest. Rising's at six and parade's at eight. The Corporal Instructor of No. 13 squad calls out the names, to which each man shouts: 'Corporal', and stamps his left foot. The Instructor's task is to turn this job-lot of clerks, shop-keepers, commercial travellers, factory-workers and odds and ends into precisely drilled automata within six weeks; and he must be strict or they will 'swing the lead' and resist the smartening-up process.

Webland, still not having discovered his fumigated spare clothes, begins to feel really dirty and uncomfortable as he sweats in the sunshine. Most sorely does he miss the hair that was left behind in the skin-hospital. He had never realized that arms and legs swinging to and fro need a lubricant, even as bearings do in machinery. Without hair the chafing soon makes raw places, and at the first opportunity he lays in a store of boracic powder, cotton-wool, sticking-plaster and a powder puff to see him through this period. How long does such hair take to grow again? There being no instant means of discovering he'll have to wait and feel.

The days pass in three forms of instruction: drill, lectures and physical training. The drill takes place on the quiet cliff-side street and crescents; the lectures in a hall or on the cliffs; and the P.T. also on the cliffs. The P.T., rumoured to be non-compulsory for the over thirty-fives, is the least agreeable, although Webland and the few other elders think it best to join in, thus:

Watched by passing civilians the squad assembles on the springy turf, takes off its tunics, caps, braces, collars and ties, exchanges its boots for purple plimsolls, called 'pumps', stuffs its trouser-ends inside its socks, and starts leaping like a jack-in-the-box. For an hour Webland jumps, hops, crouches, thrashes his arms, deep-breathes, plays leap-frog, springs on chums for piggy-backs, dashes on all fours through short men's legs – all in the heat of noonday and the same shirt and prickly trousers. When singlets and blue cotton shorts return from the disinfector, after the last squad to pass out has discarded them, he'll be able to jig about in those more comfortably. He is anxious about his knees, which have lately been getting arthritic, but they only give him a twinge after long squatting or a sudden twist.

The Corporal Instructor says they must learn *esprit de corps*. 'Anyone 'ere know the meanin' of "Esperee de cor"?' No one gives himself away. 'Well, it's a Latin word meanin' all pullin' together. Get it?' It seems that an explanation generally ends with the words 'Get it?' or 'Right?' or 'O.K.?' and no answer desired.

Webland had thought that military life would provide plenty of time for reading and writing, but here it is not so. Even if he were not too tired to read in bed at night, the black-out round the ceiling light would make it almost impossible; and that's fortunate, because with a six o'clock rising every day, sleep is the best thing for bed. An hour in which to get ready in the morning and an hour at night are none too generous. There are boots and buttons to polish every day; clothes have to be marked against loss, crumples removed from tunics, creases put into trousers by means of soap inside them and being put under the biscuits and slept on each night.

Two days later than the promised time the confiscated clothes are discovered at the stores. Webland hoists the unfriendly kit-bag on his shoulder, the overcoat on his arm, and brings them the half-mile back to his billet. A cheery civilian seeing him calls out: 'Going for your holiday?' 'Not I', the over-grammatical answer comes back, as Webland tries to shape his face into a knowing airman's leer. All kit is correct, and the shirt and under-clothes he is wearing can at last be sent to the wash. Powdered and cotton-woolled, his razor-cuts healing, with clean garments over all, he feels a better man.

The first lecture on gas was to have been given, but the Officer doesn't come. Now what's to be done? Of course; a pianist is called for from the audience, and up pops a small cockney, whom Webland has already viewed, on account of his ceaseless language of oaths and filth, with some distaste. He skips on to the platform and plays the popular radio tunes really well. It appears that he was ten years in the Navy, and is quite a talented fellow. He is known as George, although it is not his name, because that is what he calls everyone else. As Webland gets to know him, he realizes that the filthy talk is the first and least of George and is no more than a thoughtless mannerism.

An almost less attractive recruit, another cockney, is Shag, who is plainly at odds with society. The look of him rather worries Webland, especially when he can be heard in the ranks on parade delineating the parts of the woman he'd had the night before. He also mentions that he has spent some months in a Wessex jail. He is of middle height, strongly built, probably in his thirties, and with a face that the French, on the principle of *joli-laid*, might describe as strong-weak. There is something of a monkey's sadness in his fine blue eyes, and a look in them of no confidence: a hunted, punished look, wary and half-defiant. Webland recognizes the type as one he has read of who 'never had a chance in life', and feels rather proud to be in service with him, as it might be with a celebrity.

There is pleasure in a smart salute, greater than in that of a jaded hat-raising. In one morning Webland is able to salute two Colonels in one gesture. He learns that he must salute even boy cadets. Meeting a little chap of sixteen in uniform and white gloves at the counter of a shop in the town, he asks:

'Are you a Midshipman?'

'No; I'm an R.N.R. cadet.'

'We have to salute Midshipmen, but I don't think I salute you, do I?'

'Actually, I am supposed to be saluted, as a cadet.'

'Well, we haven't been taught that yet.'

One nice point of etiquette he has learnt is that a Warrant Officer is to be called 'Sir', but not saluted. Strange. The reason may become apparent later as he gets to know the breed.

The variety of talents is interesting to see gradually exposing itself from the uniform and dull-faced ranks, and, judging from gossip with Corporal Cowley, it is more impressive than anything that the Officers' Mess of the Household Cavalry could yield. In Webland's squad is a locomotive-fitter from the railway at Darlington who plays the clangy piano in the Cliffhaven with skill. He never mentioned his talent before, although at home he is an organist and choir-master. His music pleases May, the cook for fifteen lodgers, who has a hard life, and tells Webland of her problems, while he gives sage nods and comments such as 'Fancy!' and 'Never!' and 'You don't say!' She comes in to work from seven till seven, and hasn't had a half-day off in two months nor been able to visit her mother in six; and never a free Sunday. She is always jolly, though, is married to a Sergeant in the Dorsets, calls Webland 'Dear' or 'Love', and even finds time to iron his tunic when the kinks won't level out.

The service doctor has been undergone; and the service barber; now comes the service dentist. Webland is more than ever apprehensive of the consequences of him. Fifty men go for tooth-inspection, awaiting their turn on the stairs outside. The dentist shoves the same unwiped mirror into expectant mouths, one every ten seconds. In most cases he calls: 'Treatment' to the assistant with a notebook, and very rarely: 'Fit'. Webland, after his condemnation by the doctor, has lost all confidence in his health and hygiene and expects to be certified as being a repulsive case of caries and pyorrhoea, even if N.Y.D., to be detached and hurried to a surgery. 'Fit', though. Good man, this dentist. At least he knows a decent mouth when he sees one.

Keeping clean is perhaps less easy for a man who has been used to having one or two hot baths every day than for one trained at wash-rooms and scullery-coppers. 'You can't have a bath every day, you know,' says the landlord; not that the water is even lukewarm more than two nights in the week. This is to be a constant minor trouble between them. But the recruit is gradually breaking himself in to the new ways. Old fears and habits are getting dug out and dissolved. Twice he has eaten tapioca pudding with skin – his one dish of dread – and pretended to relish it. Physical fitness is coming fast, the training being well devised with that object; the hard work is never too hard; and most of the Flight seem happy.

After ten days Webland feels that he has never worn anything but uniform, and even his little cap-on-one-side is getting familiar. The fatter and the weaker – none is older than he – may suffer somewhat, but the friendliness and the laughter bear them all along together. He is beginning to think how salutary it is for every man to serve in the ranks for a spell, and wonders if he will be sad when the time comes, as it soon will, for him to leave and become an Officer. There is a nursery comfort in being in the safe care of N.C.O.s who know their job and their men, who are not without understanding of the troubles of recruits and try to help as well as train them. Such N.C.O.s, thank God, are these at Cadstone.

The Saturday of delayed inoculation arrives and Webland and one other recruit, named Swamp, are fetched away from P.T. to change back and report to the M.O. There, on the paths of an untidy kitchen-garden, they take the last two places at the end of the file of about a hundred and fifty coatless men, shirt-sleeves rolled up, and shuffle slowly round towards the door of the medical shed. The vaccination is a scratch and a piece of lint on the left arm, and then come the inoculations by syringe against tetanus and typhus: twice more round the garden, one man every three seconds. Webland recognizes in the doctor his old Levantine tormentor and expects trouble.

As each man comes by, an orderly smears the upper right arm with a yellow liquid. Then the M.O. takes over with 'Hurry up, man!' and 'Come on now, you bloody fool!' A few yards short of the shed Swamp sinks to the ground with an animal moan, is hoisted up and dragged in to the operation by two orderlies obviously well used to the job. He is suitably dealt with. As a matter of fact only six faint this day. Two files behind, another man flinches badly at the approach of the needle, the M.O. misses his mark and squirts the charge of anti-typhus into the face of the man following. The M.O.'s nerves don't seem under control:

'Jesus Christ, man, can't you stand still? You ought to

be ashamed of yourself – a bloody great hulking fellow like you!'

The man behind who had got it in the eye is hurried away to have it bathed, and the files shuffle on. Webland wonders if the M.O. will recognize him, but his eyes are on the arms. The jab is made, all is well, and he hopes to have no more meetings with this tetchy doctor. Rumour, which has an answer to everything in the services, tells him afterwards that the man was once sweet and gentle, but that a short experience of this rough life had turned him into a cynic and a bully. Not the first, no doubt, to suffer such a change.

The thing for an inoculated man to do now, says Corporal Cowley, is to take an hour's walk, swinging the stiffening arm vigorously so as to swirl the stuff round the blood-stream as soon as possible. This done, aspirins and bed will take care of the ensuing shivers, and Bob, as they say, is your uncle. The relationship proves to be correct, and Webland wakes up on Sunday morning fit and every inch Bob's nephew.

He is still, however, unsure of his position here as his father's son. The day before yesterday the Sergeant who drills the whole Flight had asked him, unheard by the others, if it was a fact that he was something to do with Montagu Webland, and made no comment on the reply. This evening a roughish-looking recruit called Flanagan, whom Webland had already classed as a potential rebel, says to him:

'Excuse me asking, but is it true you're Montagu Webland's son?'

Webland nods cautiously.

'Then you're a visscount, aren't yer?'

This surprisingly good shot at the complicated canons of the British nobility, though not perfectly accurate, and the delicate manner in which it has been stalked for, melt Webland's first reserve, and there follows a pleasant chat on that aspect of social life. Flanagan supposes that of course Webland has no need to work, which is in a literal sense true but practically not so. Webland tries to explain something of the financial and ethical issues involved in such an inheritance as his own and they part with mutual understanding and respect, especially warm on Webland's side when he is complimented by this gruff charmer on the way he has chosen to rough it with the chaps. Truly, here's hidden treasure that Webland and his sort, with all their education, might pass their whole lives with never a sight of. Has he really joined, instead of a troop of ruffians as he'd feared, a flight of thickly-disguised angels? Why are they all so understanding? Will this grace also melt away with the trailing wisps of civilian innocence still to be detected in their uniform behaviour? As the N.C.O.s say with their words of command: 'Wait for it!'

A fresh week of work begins. Webland has investigated his relative position in the country's armed forces. He is an airman of the lowest rank, Aircraftman or A/C2, in a Squad, which is part of a Flight, which is part of a Recruit Centre, of which there may be dozens in the British Isles. It is late September and the weather is still warm and bright. The time-table of this second Monday of training runs on.

The usual parade in the road from eight until half-past nine. A lecture sitting on the cliff-grass until ten. A break for a cup of tea and a bun or a piece of cake until half-past. A march to buses for the weekly forced bath in the town. At noon, a medical inspection to see which vaccinated left arms haven't taken. After lunch, drill by Flight, not Squad. Another lecture, followed by P.T., in which is played a game something like Hunt the Slipper, but standing and running, in which the slipper-man is chased round the ring and struck with a belt; other beneficial and breath-taking exercises are done for an hour, wearing old singlets and faded blue shorts, and watched by many laughing townsfolk. Dismissal at five o'clock for a stretch of private polishing of best and worst boots.

At the public baths three or four naked men stand closely pressed under the shower. Dressing in the

cubicle takes Webland a long time, as he has to replace
sticking-plaster on his punctured arm, fit lint on each
inner ankle inside his socks where the boots have chafed,
and much more lint and plaster in between his thighs
where sores and itchings have arisen since the great shave
and have been excoriated by the long and sweaty drilling
in hot weather.

There is a thief among the angels, or perhaps some
devilish outsider, for the landlord has lost his wallet from
his coat pocket, with identity card, driving-licence and
£25; and a man of Webland's Squad in the neighbouring
billet has had his dispatch-case taken, containing the
wife's letters and his private business papers. Webland
decides to lock his small brown case and carry the key
with him, though that will not prevent the key being
lost or the case removed. Suspicion, of course, must
fall on Shag, who might well be above such petty dishonesty, as he grunts with consummate contempt that
he is.

Webland goes to bed that night pleased with the day's
doings. Standing a bare six feet, he is not the tallest
recruit, yet he has been picked to be right-hand man of
the Flight of six Squads and, though it may sound catas-
trophic, they all 'fall in' on him alone. The well-known
alleged starting order of N.C.O.s: 'Get fell in there!' is
always good for a laugh among the more grammatical
recruits, though Webland has yet to hear the phrase in its
authentic purity.

Some light has been thrown on the subject of fainting
by a quiet Scotchman, who explained how he himself
had been affected when he fell unconscious eight times
queueing round the cabbage-patch to the medical shed that
day. He had no fear of the needle and had fainted only
once before in his life, which happened when someone
who had very recently undergone an anaesthetic breathed
cigarette smoke at him. He thinks that these faintings are
caused by the vapour from the liquid smeared on his
own and other men's arms. He felt perfectly well all the

time, and on each occasion sank pleasantly to the ground in the course of conversation.

One of Webland's many absurd fears of life in the ranks had been that he might be unable to stand long in the sun. One or two men have fallen out in the heat already, but Webland finds he can stand rock-still, and his skin that he thought so tender is not being badly burned by the salty rays of the seaside sun. It may be the wholesome and none too plentiful food that has improved his stamina. It may also be the will to stand all that's to be stood.

Sooner than expected appears the first chance of promotion. At the end of the day's work a Sergeant announces that those who want to apply for commissions are to ask for a form to fill in. Seeing that four or five undistinguished-looking older recruits in the Flight wait behind afterwards, Webland thinks he will also; he does so; and a note is made of their names. The rumour in the ranks is that, after one has been interviewed successively by higher and higher Officers for a period of weeks, one goes to be interviewed finally in London and is asked what school one was at and what games one plays.

Webland has not met anyone in the same situation as himself: that is to say, preferring to try for a commission from the bottom with no previous attempt to begin as an Officer. These R.A.F. applicants, it seems, have already tried and been refused before having been conscripted into the ranks. His way of doing it may take weeks, or even months, to materialize, but meanwhile the life is good, salubrious alike for psychological cases and for aristocrats. Having seen how his comrades are helping him to be housemaid, valet and general knockabout man, he can face an uncommissioned year without anxiety. Bash on, then.

The Flight and the Squads are still feeling their way from entity to identity. The awkward and the shy are partly concealed in the middle files, and the smarter are becoming noticed by the N.C.O.s. More than once Webland has been picked out, both in mass Flight and in

Squad drill, to be end-man of the line. On a march the Corporal has appointed him Right Hand Man of the front file to give tone, precision and swing to the Flight. 'Webland, you change places with the end man!' Webland is pleased because he knows he can do the drill, less pleased because he wonders if the displaced end-man will dislike him for it. On the march back in column of threes he and his two colleagues are in the rear, but after some graceless progress, stopping and starting afresh again and again, the Corporal loses patience, sends the front file in disgrace to the rear and substitutes Webland's file at the head once more. After it is over, one of the second file of three says to him: 'By God, what a difference marching behind you after those other blokes slopping and wobbling about in front of us!'

Webland in his responsible position as fugleman feels like a carriage-horse who keeps swivelling an ear backwards to catch any word of command, which, in a long column of marchers, is sometimes bawled rather indistinctly from fifty yards behind through the sounds of tramping boots, motor traffic and often howls and barks from N.C.O.s of other passing Squads. Also within his range of hearing are the occasional mutters out of the depth of the files from Shag and the two or three ungovernable malcontents.

But Shag's sad blue eyes and sly dogged look are already beginning to arouse Webland's sympathy, however much he deplores this alarming practice of talking in the ranks; but he avoids standing near him on parade, for the Corporal is getting angry about what he calls 'nattering', and there may be trouble. 'I'll *shake* you!' is a regular N.C.O.'s threat, though what form the shaking will assume has yet to be seen.

With the others Webland calls Shag 'Shaggy'. Since it seems plain that Shaggy is stubbornly fighting a losing battle against an unkind world and will never surrender, Webland cannot help admiring the irrepressible courage of the man to count for something, somewhere. Soon

44

Shaggy asks him the inevitable question: was Montagu Webland really his dad? ''E's in Canada, ain't 'e?' Once more Webland explains the false report, and Shaggy, himself so often misunderstood, seems to understand. He and some others, though, continue to address Webland as Mr Webland; but this practice will have to be discontinued.

After two weeks of patient polishing, about twenty hours' work, the high gleam on the toes of Webland's best boots starts to flake off in small patches. This is disastrous. He has more or less mastered all the rest of the recruit-craft, but he cannot come to an understanding with these boots and their unnatural gloss. In his despair along comes Corporal Cowley, who at once diagnoses the fault, goes upstairs to fetch his own cleaning materials and for over an hour works magic upon them: magic learned at Knightsbridge Barracks on thigh-high cavalry jack-boots, which had earned him the shiniest pair in the regiment. Greater than the sense of relief at boots saved, of gratitude even, is the honour of the action; as though, Webland felt, he had been rowed across the Serpentine by the First Sea Lord. And this action was quite selfless, for the Corporal was not even connected with Webland's Flight, and could therefore be brought no credit whatsoever thereby. In poignant parenthesis, he learns that Corporal Cowley has practically no money and a very sick wife in hospital.

This not uncommon state of personal affairs, and the cheerfulness with which it is borne, causes Webland to reflect upon all the silver spoons in the well-born mouths, such as his own, and the insolence of his past self-pity. His brain charged with these swarms of new impressions, he doesn't fall asleep that night as quickly as his bodily fatigue demands. The past day's events come crowding up for selection and imprinting: the social fortitude of the poor, for instance, which he had long been dimly aware of and sometimes witnessed, but never so closely as now; the names of the small parts of a rifle, from the upper-sling-swivel to the cocking-piece; the fact that a Wing-Commander equals a Lieutenant-Colonel who equals a Naval Commander; whether to salute a passing coffin at attention or merely give it an 'Eyes Right'. These matters fill his mind entirely. How quick and absolute has been the change of values in three sharp weeks!

'Special inspection in the morning,' the Flight Sergeant announces. 'Bring your spare boots well polished' – God save Corporal Cowley and his black magic yesterday – 'buttons bright, and all get your hair cut tonight.' Boots: all correct, or, as this language of letters goes, orl korrect, O.K. Buttons: easy. Hair: it's a fortnight since his was cut; so off he dashes to a barber's shop where he finds one scalp in the chair and six waiting. It's five o'clock and the shop shuts at six-thirty. The barber says he had no customers at all in the afternoon, and yet four of these people waiting are a parson, two little boys and a needless youth. Blast these civilians, why can't they come when it's less convenient for them?

Having an hour and a quarter to wait, he strolls along the street and thinks he will buy some writing-paper. For a few pence extra, says the shop-girl, you can buy a pad 'With your crest on it'.

'Crest?'

'Yes: R.A.F.'

'Oh, I thought you meant my family crest.' And he did. Clearly she considers Webland a most amusing airman.

He gets his hair cut, though a short, rough cut it is: no questions asked, no suggestions proffered.

In the muggy heat of the morning's drill the Corporal is in a bad mood, the men stale, and A/C Webland disgusted with his own performance, mishearing commands from far away, as they all turn and stamp and double-march until they are drenched with sweat. It is a relief when a Sergeant calls out all those who have applied for commissions to march, led by Webland, not only in step but for the first time in voice: 'Party – Right Wheel!'

'Party – Halt!' and so on, to Wing Headquarters. A Warrant Officer in the presence of the men's Flight Sergeant, asks each a few questions and decides whether to pass him on for a higher interview. Three minutes suffice for Webland, and he is passed. That takes an hour of waiting; standing of course.

Outside, with the nine other aspirants, none of them from the higher levels of civilian society, the Flight Sergeant asks Webland if it is true that he is Lord Webland's son. He adds that it had soon been discovered when Webland had first arrived at Cadstone, 'So,' he adds, 'you're a marked man.' By this he may mean no more than a jest, but the men seem to approve of the situation and smile cordially.

There follows, after the tea and bun break and two more hours of standing, another interview, this time with the Adjutant in the presence of that same Warrant Officer. The Adjutant, an elderly Army ex-Major asks Webland what school he has been at and something of his pre-war career. It is evident that he knows why Webland is a marked man, and he says he will pass on a recommendation to the Group Captain, and then, if all goes well, will come one from the Group Captain to the A.O.C. The final passing is to be done by the Air Ministry in London. Afterwards he wonders why he was not asked for his School Certificate, as all his mates had been. Perhaps he wore such a certificated air that it was taken as given.

Keen to find out what A.O.C. stands for, Webland, on his return to the billet, seeks out Corporal Cowley. Learning that the Corporal has gone to South Wales with a draft – 'Gone with the wind,' says Mr Bolt, the jolliest of the civil servants – he hopes it means nothing lasting. If this splendid young godfather were to be posted away for ever he would be acutely missed. A substitute informant is pretty sure that A.O.C. means Air Officer Commanding: empyrean title indeed.

That long day had been one of good and bad, thoroughly typical of a serviceman's life: severe toil and much waiting in a hut and staring at a wall. Bad in the morning's drill, good in the interviews, bad in the gaps of timeless standing, good and bad in the P.T., bad in the waiting at the barber's and plush-cropped back of the head, bad in the disappointment of Corporal Cowley's absence.

P.T. had been more distasteful than usual. Playing piggy-back Webland had been ridden by a specially dirty jockey. Then he, in his turn, had had to jump on to a much smaller man's back and piaffe round like a drunken centaur. Dismounted, then, a kind of serpent was created, hands round the stomach of the man in front, another man's round his, the object being to hit blindfolded men who were made to pass between two lines, the stricken heads having to guess who had hit them. The cliffs rang with civil and military laughter.

Webland is plainly a subject of interest to the junior authorities as well as to his equals. The Sergeant asks him: 'What were you before this? A gentleman of leisure?' When Webland explains that it has been necessary to earn money in order to keep a wife and children, the Sergeant's disbelieving comment is: 'But yer father's got millions, hasn't he?' 'Good Lord, no, Sergeant, not one million nor the half of one.' Have the newspapers supplied the notion or did it just grow? There's no ill-feeling here, anyway.

The men think they are not getting as much to eat as they would if they were in camp on military rations. Webland never rises from the table replete; and at the other billets down the road, where mess most of his Squad, they only have one barely sufficient meal, in the middle of the day, the other two, breakfast and supper, being much too scanty for hard-marching men. Blancmange and bread and cocoa, for example, isn't much of a high tea between one-thirty and a thin, cold breakfast next morning at seven; and that breakfast isn't much to sustain them until one o'clock dinner, even counting a cup of tea and a bun that can be bought at the ten o'clock morning break – if they do get a break, which is never certain. At the Cliffhaven, with Corporal Cowley and the civil servants lodging there, the feeding is less mean, and Webland can always find the cash, if he can't always find the time, to buy a bit more in the shops. But those men who can barely afford sixpence – and there are some – for boot and button-polish and hair-cuts every ten days have to be paid for – do have a lean time if the billetor happens to be stingy.

Mr Procket has been judged by the men to be making money out of their hunger, and they seek means of revenge. At the morning break, when Jenkins proffers a two shilling piece for his tea and bun, Davis, who acts as salesman for the hated landlord, serving behind the counter and handling the cash, gives Jenkins two and sixpence by way of change. 'Go on, man,' he says, 'the old robber can afford it.' Jenkins tells Webland that an airman in his squad, an ex-policeman, has been sending home linen he had found in a cupboard at his billet, by way of spiting the profiteer and helping his own family at the same time.

There is no delay over the commission applications, and within twenty-four hours of having seen the Adjutant a four-page form has to be filled in, stating history and qualifications. While he is furrowing over his application form in the Flight Sergeant's room at Headquarters, he is sent for by the Commanding Officer of the Wing, Squadron Leader Hooper. Evidently the Adjutant had passed up the news of this recruit's unusual situation, because the C.O., after speaking of that for a minute or two, asks Webland's advice, as it were man to businessman on a matter of private difficulty, and sends him away with some papers to study. This is a self-respecting hour for Webland, and he hopes he will be able to show his civilian acumen. The interview ends with his being asked whether he had applied previously for a commission. When asked why not, he doesn't feel able to explain to this good-natured C.O. the complicated reasons that have led him to go in at the bottom. He decides to give an approximation by saying: 'It seemed rather feeble to put in for a commission right away, sir.'

Fired by the interview, after high tea he offers to relieve the airman who should be doing fatigue at the billet but wants to go out that evening. The man's target may be the Naffy just along the road, always full of a clattering, smoking throng, with a piano in the corner sounding an off-harmony like banjoes and church bells; or it may be that softer one which he has been warned against by the padre and the doctor.

The fatigue is probably only washing-up, at which Webland thinks he will not fail. The kitchen is under-staffed, there being but one scullery girl who has to drudge all day and serve anything from twelve to twenty eaters.

It is announced that from next Monday parades are to start earlier, at seven-forty-five and not finish until five-thirty. No one knows why, for the men have really quite enough exercise. They wonder if anyone is going to get up early to give them breakfast; because, if not, it will be no joke drilling all the morning on no food: a situation not unknown here already. But the R.A.F. commanders, it is said, are quick to look after their men's health and food and board, and they come down heavily on the bad landlords and ladies.

This Sunday Webland, having misinformed himself that there was to be a Church Parade at ten-thirty, joined about a hundred recruits under a few N.C.O.s and is marched to a Methodist church where are heard five hymns, two sermons, three prayers and a lesson. He cannot understand this apostasy until he discovers that the Church of England men paraded at nine-fifteen and the later ones were all lumped into a group called O.D., which stands for Other Denominations. Afterwards it is the custom in this area for the R.A.F. and the A.T.S, who are soldier-women, to walk severally up and down and round and about in twos and threes, both teams desiring the companionship of the other sex and seeking an overture to the performance of clicking.

Several men in the Squad have invited their wives down for a weekend or even for the rest of the training period. The women stay in the lodging house billets and wear the most creditable clothes possible. Any lesser garb would be unthinkable, for in a sense this is a passing-out parade of the better half and nothing but the best will do. One wife wears silver-fox furs and another is attached by leads to two little dogs. Webland, who is reminded of when one's people came down on a half-holiday at school, had not thought of his own wife in these circumstances, any more than having her to live in his London club; and he still thinks it unseemly.

He is picking up the lingo. First in importance are the countless initials, because they are official, and it is unconceivable that the full words should be in use. No one is going to have time to refer to the Non-Commissioned Officers or the Navy Army and Air Force Institute. The abbreviations are easy to memorize. The slang is unnecessary to use, but it is as well to understand it, because many men can't find any other words with which to express themselves. Webland is more interested in the origins of the phrases, but there are no means of finding these out, so he has to imagine them.

Unpleasant tasks are called 'binding' or 'being a bind'. Being jaded is 'feeling browned off', or sometimes 'cheesed off' or 'brassed off'. Instructions or information are known as 'gen', or, more rarely, 'griff'. 'Gen', he imagines, might come from 'genuine', as opposed to spurious, tidings. Tall men are called 'Lofty' – 'is it cold up there?' – short men 'Shorty', orange-haired men 'Ginger', lanky men 'Bones' or even 'Dog's Dinner', fat men 'Tubby', any man in the ranks 'Charley': 'Hey you, Charley.' 'Speak up, Charley.'

Webland first met the phrase 'You've had it' from the rude mouth of the Sergeant who had received him on first reporting for duty at his call-up; and it baffled him. He had been told by the Officer at his pre-call-up interview near home that he would be put into the special administrative branch, which seemed reasonable – or, as the jargon goes, 'fair enough'. But six weeks later on reporting for duty this curt Sergeant, having asked him which branch he was down for, said, 'You've 'ad it.' Incomprehensible.

'What happens, then?' Webland asked.

'You better choose another branch.'

Webland didn't know the name of any other branch, so he said: 'What are they? I mean, could you give me a list to choose from?'

The Sergeant wasn't pleased, but he rapidly read out technical R.A.F. trades, and when he got to Radio Telephone Operator Webland stopped him and said he thought he would choose that one. At least he could telephone, and probably soon learn the radio and the operator parts. So into the service he went as a potential telephonist or R.T.O., which can also, by the way, stand for Railway Transport Officer in the Army.

But 'You've had it'; that was a phrase that must be understood before using. Evidently it meant 'You've not had it, and you're not going to have it'. But why? In the course of the first weeks Webland had asked here and there, but no one knew. At last someone gave him a reasonable explanation. It seems that there was once at a ball a couple who, so far as the girl was concerned, had just completed an unsatisfactory dance together. The man, however, being charmed by his partner and keen to dance again, said to her, 'Can't we have another one?' She put him off with excuses, until he said: 'Well, can't I have the *last* dance with you?' She, both truthfully and heartlessly, replied: 'You've had it.'

Now in that sense, Webland thought, it makes great sense; but as used by the Sergeant over the administrative post or by anyone refusing any application at all, it was merely untrue; unless by universal consent it became raised to the status of a dead witticism, and employed as a smart substitute for the word 'No'. Incidentally Webland finds that the words 'Yes' and 'No' are seldom used in military circles, where something more forceful is considered desirable, something indicative of strength of purpose and total command of one's subject. Therefore one answers either: 'Definitely, sir', or 'Definitely not, sir', and honour is satisfied.

The commission game goes on. When will someone say: 'You've had it'? Webland is rather anxious about the form that he has sent in. This fourth Monday morning of his service the applicants are to report again to H.Q. at 9 a.m.

They stand in the passage downstairs until ten, then, by suggestion of the Flight Sergeant, sit upstairs smoking until eleven, when they are told to report back at two. At two the C.O. receives them for the purpose of seeing that the four-page form has been filled in correctly. He doesn't think two of Webland's answers will do: 'Given up games' for 'Sport and games played', and 'Can't Remember' for 'School Certificate Subjects'. Not altogether repressing the temptation to tease this military form, Webland re-writes his answers in a less off-hand style. For Sport and games he puts: 'Cricket, Football, Racquets, Squash Racquets, Tennis, Lawn Tennis, Golf, Fives, Shooting, Swimming, Skating, Skiing'; which was true so far as it went, but not so far as to indicate which of them he had played fairly well and which not well at all. For the School Certificate he hazards Greek, Latin, French, Divinity, Mathematics and History, but he has no means of checking his memory. These answers seem to satisfy the friendly C.O., who instructs him to report again at 9 a.m. tomorrow, an hour at which he is supposed to be doing his fortnightly fatigue of washing-up, laying tables, cleaning rooms, peeling potatoes and disposing of garbage.

All this reporting at H.Q. is taking him away from training, and he is not sorry to be in time to join the Flight for a bayonet-fighting lecture on the cliffs. Luckily he has just missed the P.T. horse-play. There is nothing much to be learned from those cliff-top games, and anyway it has been established that P.T. is not compulsory for those over thirty-five.

It is apparent that smartness at drill is not going to bring a recruit's commission any closer. The Officers don't watch to see if one is smart or not; it is the paper form concerning education and civilian experience that seems to count. But this realization doesn't lessen Webland's wish to succeed, and he continues the search for excellence. When marching at attention fingers must be curled, not clenched, thumbs uppermost, unbent arms swinging level with the shoulders, while the N.C.O. shouts: 'Up, up, up, up! Left, right, left, right! One, two, three, four! Reach back! Up, up!' Marching at ease, the ranks are allowed to whistle and sing, and, led by the Welsh, he joins in tunes old and new, familiar and unknown. The old march, 'Blaze Away', is very popular; so are Grandfather's Clock', 'Ilkley Moor', 'Coming round the Mountain' and 'I've got Sixpence'.

Not a bad life, this, for a growing lad. Not bad either for the likes of Theodore Webland.

4
All the Best

Fellowship is life, and lack of fellowship is death;
and the deeds that ye do upon the Earth, it is for
fellowship's sake that ye do them.
WILLIAM MORRIS – *A Dream of John Bull*

To the joy of all at the Cliffhaven, knightly, wise, immaculate Corporal Cowley is back. September marches
off, bequeathing its month-long sunshine; and the
recruits, in high morale, are half-way through their course.

The Flight is sorry to lose its Flight Sergeant, once a
steel-worker in the North of England, who is about to be
posted to a course at Wolverhampton. These high N.C.O.s
are regarded as almost omniscient, and it seems an impertinence for them to be posted for further training.
Their Flight Sergeant sincerely has the future welfare of
his airmen on his mind and, before being torn from them,
he sits them down on the turf and talks to them with
fatherly charm, warning them of the pitfalls in the open
world.

It is a masterly address of about three-quarters of an
hour, and the gist and the motto of it in his own closing
words are: 'Self first, self last; and if there's anything over
put it in your pocket.' Fascinating to listen to and carrying all the authority of a contented long-serviceman, it is
threaded with anecdotes of success achieved by scrounging, deceiving, misrepresenting, listening at doors, which
practices are said to make all the difference between getting

something out of the Service or nothing. On the older listeners the reaction is uncertain, but on the younger probably decisive. Everyone likes the Flight Sergeant, and Webland is honoured when he says he'll be coming along to him for a job after the war. 'Cheero, lads!' 'All the best, Flight!'

At the start of October Webland's Squad has a change of Corporal Instructors. The new one, Corporal Eves, is fresh from an Instructors' Drill Course, and full of vigour, discipline and impatience. It is his evident intention to ginger up No. 13 to be the smartest Squad in the Flight, and Webland and his friends guess they are in for a strenuous time. The triers, though, are not dismayed, for he won't be hard on them. His eyes will be on the slackers, known as 'stooges' or 'scroungers'.

'Now then,' he says, 'I want bags of bullshit.' This stock term for exaggerated swagger and smartness no doubt derives from an idea in the ranks of its supposed uselessness. It is not a perfect simile, but it has caught on, perhaps because of the rude splendour of the words. And to head the new order, after trying three or four of the tallest men for Right Marker, the Corporal finally chooses Webland. The reason for this may be partly that Webland's boots, not like some being rubber soled, make a good crash on the ground when he stamps his feet. It is plain that you can't produce firm bullshit out of soft boots.

For the first time in three weeks there is a cold wind and a scurry of rain. At P.T. on the cliffs the thin shorts and singlets are judged to be inadequate protection for the weaker flesh and bones of the men over thirty-five, so they are ordered to put their clothes on again while the younger ones are sent off for a run westward into the weather, to return in twenty minutes wet, warm and breathless to their guarded tunics. Thus does the Service care for the health of all ages in what it calls 'inclement weather', with the epithet sounded as a dactyl, rhyming with increment.

Corporal Cowley has been offered an old bicycle for £3,

but he doesn't want to pay so much, so Webland has agreed to pay half on condition that he can ride it at week-ends. He doesn't expect to do so, but he might. The bicycle is to become the Corporal's property when Webland finishes the square-bashing course and is posted.

Next day comes Webland's turn for a day's fatigue down the street at the Squad's main feeding place. It is a bit unquiet down there, for they still aren't getting enough food and the civilian serving-man isn't co-operating, so they revile him. He had to lock himself up in a room the other day when he was threatened, and this very morning an irritated Aberdonian has thrown a can of cocoa over him. By this time Webland is confident in his ability to get on with almost all types, and he looks forward to this day off parade, from eight to six, waiting at tables, helping the cook, washing-up and cleaning all round. He doesn't mind missing drill now, being confirmed in the estimation of the N.C.O.s and well up in general progress.

At eight o'clock in the morning Webland presents himself for fatigue duty at 9 Priscilla Avenue, where the rest of the Squad feed and the shindies get kicked up, gives his name and asks the cook and the scullion waiter what his orders are. They are ready for him, having heard something of him from the airmen, and both give indications of wishing to treat him with latitude. Mrs Hackett, the cook, is a stern, elderly woman from Bermondsey who has been bombed out of her home. She can deal easily with any riot of recruits, or with anyone else, giving oath for oath and perhaps blow for blow; but to Webland she is as sweet as can be all the long day through. Although at the start she tries to call him 'Tommy', she can't keep it up and only manages 'Sir' or 'Mr Webland'. She won't let him demean himself by cleaning the kitchen floor, so she allows him to peel some earthy potatoes, with a peeler and a pail of water. He does this with increasing skill on and off during the day for about five hours.

Between ten and eleven o'clock he helps to hand out

tea and sixty dozen buns to the rush of recruits and N.C.O.s
during the break between parades. Then he washes up
and dries quantities of cups and spoons and plates. He
gets closely acquainted with dark nooks where lie potato-
peel, paper, dust, ashes and old wet tea-leaves: general
back-yard slurry, the sight of which had once depressed
him, but now does so no longer because it seems but the
material of his newly acquired craft to be dealt with as
efficiently as possible.

The scullion waiter tells him that it is an honour to
have him working there; that they had had all sorts at
Cadstone, even the son of a Sir; and that he himself hadn't
always worked in a kitchen, for his father was vicar of a
country parish; and out from his pocket comes a photo-
graph of the old man. He doesn't explain how he had
reached his present civilian post from such a reverend
start, but he explains that he and his less agreeable wife,
who has been fidgeting round the kitchen all day doing
very little work, belong to a religious sect which holds
Sunday on Saturday, thus procuring, so the rumour runs,
two holidays per week.

If this is fatigue, thinks Webland, then there should be
a pleasanter name for it. Perhaps the discovery that Mrs
Hackett had once been cook to an old friend of Webland's
in London has put their relationship on a more indulgent
footing than it might have been; although it is true that
she had never been other than friendly to him from the
beginning. Moreover, the length of the day has been broken
by yet another visit to the M.I. (Medical Inspection) Room
in connexion with his application for a commission.

Here the doctor sets about his task less churlishly than
before, perhaps because of the likelihood of the inspected
bodies soon becoming of more social consequence. He
has evidently forgotten Webland and his chimerical crabs
when he praises the condition of his teeth. He tests his
eyes, his ears, his nasal passages, his chest and his back.
He scrapes his thighs and the soles of his feet, hits his
knees and Achilles tendons for reactions, makes him say

'Ah', weighs him, pokes areas of his stomach, orders him to urinate – 'jimmy riddle' is the airmen's word for it – into a wine glass over a sink and passes him fit to be an officer.

The commission is getting nearer and soon Webland is to go before the Group Captain in the neighbouring town. It looks as easy as a snakeless game of Snakes and Ladders. In a month he should reach the last throw and be out at the top.

The pace of training is being quickened. The new Corporal is the strictest of them all, but the men like him and know he is only after the sluggards and those who look browned off. There are rifles now to carry, the plain foot drill having been mastered, and packs and trinkets are attached to the uniform covering contracted paunches and strengthened muscles.

The nights are getting cooler, but every morning brings a full sun and hazy horizon heat all the strenuous day. By 7.45 as usual the squads assemble for parade. The first word of command from the Corporal is 'Marker!', at which Webland jumps to attention, detaches himself from the crowd of recruits, stamps forward six paces, stops, stands at ease with a crash, and motionless awaits the next act. 'On Parade,' shouts the Corporal, and the twenty-six others of the Squad step forth and line up in threes against Webland as he stamps to attention. When they have all got their dressing by him, he listens for the shuffling and fidgeting to cease, then he stamps his left foot to the side 'at ease', and the stamp is taken up *arpeggio presto* all down the line. There follows inspection by Corporal, or perhaps Sergeant, for bright buttons, bright boots, bright cap-badge, straight cap, straight belt, clean and uncrumpled tunic, brushed and creased trousers, hair cut short at the back almost to invisibility. Then off in column of threes to the drilling ground, which is some untrafficked avenue or square in the neighbourhood.

At rifle drill that morning, Corporal Eves is barely able to keep his patience with the sluggards and dullards. He must have had his eye on Webland too, for he says: 'Webland, ever done any rifle drill before?'

'Yes, Corporal, but not for about twenty years.'

'Christ!' For the Corporal was in his early twenties himself. 'How much of it?'

'About ten years on and off.' He didn't add that, unless you count those earliest days in the K.R.A., he'd never been drilled by anyone lower than a Sergeant of the Rifles or the Guards.

The Corporal pulls a face of wry admiration and says: 'Come out here and show these fellows how it's done.'

The pre-war Webland would have hesitated, but he now steps smartly out beside the Corporal, muttering about not being sure of getting the modern drill exact.

'Carry on and Slope Arms.' Then down to the 'Order'; and so on; all done with precise bang, slap and éclat, luckily right at the top of his form. This is Webland's apotheosis. Would that Roland and the ghosts of Sergeant Lilley and all those other O.T.C. Sergeants could see their indifferent Private at this hour!

The Corporal summons out a dull recruit who can't get the hang of the thing and is made to perform in all his ungainliness. The contrast proving satisfactory, the drill proceeds in smoother style thereafter.

On dismissal, Webland's mates, with many a joke about his being the Corporal's pet, declare that he had done the rifle movements better than the Corporal himself. To have gained the favour of his instructor without having lost the goodwill of his colleagues is gratifying and ample compensation for the extra punctuality and smartness that he has to sustain as the Squad's Marker.

He is now well settled in to the routine and at ease with his equals and superiors. He has no inferiors. What he finds so unusually pleasant is that all seem to take their fellows as they find them, even in the case of poor Shag, the malefactor, who makes himself conspicuous by his lack of discipline and complains of the Corporal: 'What's 'e always want to pick on *me* for?' So sunny is the temper of the Squad that Shaggy is treated merely as the joke, and not the plague, of it. Webland likes it very much when he is called 'Ole Webby' by Shag and some of the others, and he occasionally contrives a knowing wink as from one who could be the devil of a lad if he weren't so old and respectable.

He has a pact with his next man in the Squad, a cockney van driver called Stan, which affords some amusement. When the Corporal asks the Squad in general a question such as: 'Have you been taught to "Change Arms" yet?' instead of both of them answering 'No, Corporal!' Webland will say 'No' and Stan will rapidly follow with 'Corporal!', as if only one man had answered. Or perhaps, as late as a second or two after Webland's 'No', Stan will add an absent-minded 'Corporal!' Such small japes help to keep them all happy. Unfortunately, half-way through the course the Squad is re-graded for height, and Stan is placed at the far end of the line. With mock ceremony they shake hands and bid one another an affecting goodbye.

More horse-making equipment has been issued in grey webbing, two items of which are known technically as 'kicking traces'. It is a kind of cat's cradle puzzle to arrange and here again Corporal Cowley, who had fallen off their bicycle that day and cut his hand, helps in the evening to sort it out and put it together by name. The harness will only be worn as the day of accomplishment approaches.

This day of Passing Out, in drill, P.T., questions, et cetera, which is fixed for the 20th October, marks the change from recruit to airman proper, though the airman will still be classed untrained or u/t. There will then be a posting to some part of the British Isles for a technical training period of anything from six weeks to six months, but before the end of that period Webland is certain his commission will have come through. Yet he feels in no hurry for it, for he would rather like to sample camp or barrack life as a development from this only semi-military life in billets.

The language of letters is being easily absorbed, and also the language of numbers. A Leave Pass, for example, is referred to as a 'Two-Nine-Five', the identity card as a 'Twelve-Fifty', after which is his own national number 1338401, R.A.F. number 4121107, Squad, Flight, Squadron and Group numbers, and plenty more. He is now so deeply injected with regulations that his youthful apprehensive dreams of trouble at school have been displaced by new dreams of military deficiency and crime. Last night he dreamt that he was arrested by the S.P., which he thinks means Service Police, at Waterloo Station where he was found slinking round the back edges of platforms having no pass to be absent from his unit. Not a trace of his years on the Railway Board filtered through from the subconscious into his dream to give him a hint of his old civilian rights and authorities. It is strange to observe what enlistment, conscription and discipline can effect in a mere few weeks.

A mile walk into the town last evening with Corporal Cowley to get photographed was an exalting experience of its kind. The Corporal has a way with men and women, and many an A.T.S. girl lobs him a love-sick look and a coy remark as they pass. They all know him by sight, for he has been drilling Flights of recruits all through the summer, as he stands in his tall, dark elegance on the sea-wall, and the cliffs of Cadstone ring with his despairing cry to the Squad: 'Oh, you *stupid things*!'

Alas, though, for the haunted boots which both of them have been working on for so long and are having their first outing. Most of the polish has exploded: flipped off like enamel when metal is bent. They look piebald: part shiny, part dull. This means very hard work ahead. Webland's heart is in his boots.

He certainly feels more masterful wearing boots than purple pumps, although he has found that in nimbleness and speed of running and reaction, he is better than most at the jumping games. He is encouraged, too, by his appointment on one occasion as end-man of the P.T.

Flight of a hundred and sixty, and as such must show no sign of apathy.

But Hey Presto! during P.T. another wad of money vanished from one of the men's discarded uniforms on the cliff. All are searched, but nothing found. Poor old Shaggy is privately suspected once more; but there may well be meaner fingers than his at large in the Flight, fingers on the clean paws of some dog with no bad name attached to him.

Next comes the ordeal by gas. Webland has recently exchanged his tortoise-shell spectacles for a pair of steel ones specially fabricated for service wear with a gas-mask. Inside the gas chamber the Sergeant muffle-hoots from beneath his mask: 'Are you all getting a hundred per cent protection?' Only Webland gives out a stifled 'No, Sergeant!' and explains the cause of the leak through his spectacles' frame. The harmless gas merely makes his eyes smart. At least he has been taught to name the six parts of the face-piece, the four parts of the outlet-valve, and the filtering and absorbing elements, even if their operation doesn't keep the gas out.

There follows a lecture on bayonet fighting and hand-to-hand unarmed fighting for your life against a hypothetically dirty fighter referred to as 'Jerry'. This craft is taught by a Sergeant, once a wrestling champion, named Daly: bull-necked, cauliflower-eared, the very personification of violence, yet not entirely unmeltable.

He demonstrates the repulsive technique in the middle of a ring of recruits, then picks a man out every few minutes to dance the death dance with him. Webland keeps in the back row, but is eventually summoned for a bout of parrying the Sergeant's bayonet thrust with his rifle-butt. There is no escape, so he puts on his best act, lunging and striking like a cobra, to the approbation of his mates. Afterwards two of them tell him he is the Squad's star turn for any enterprise. They say that the Squad's feeling is expressed thus: 'Any volunteers?' 'Yes, Corporal: Webland, Corporal!' Thank heavens as a boy he had never been slow on the ball: in games and war the fatal defect.

Another successful week is over. Knocking off on Saturday at one o'clock is utterly delicious. The release from physical labour and tight constriction is sharp and absolute, and far more satisfying than weekly release from the tension of office life, which never really used to feel complete. Webland hears himself whistling as he strides back to his billet: a performance he can't remember having given since he was a child. Can perfect health account for it? The only slight faults in that are superficial: his tender vaccination scratch and the still padded sores; and those will pass.

On Sunday he sets out for his first day off, with leave to travel within a ninety mile radius, so long as he is back by eleven that night. He has decided to visit a friend in the next county. Buying his third-class return ticket he reflects that he has not bought a railway ticket for nearly five years. He had been accustomed to travelling everywhere in England on a pass, which he had naturally left at home. The ticket costs seven and fivepence: a big slice out of his unpunctual pay. He hopes he will meet the Service Police, be suspected of being absent without leave and confound them. On the way back this occurs. Two S.P.s, trained to scrutinize railway platforms, ask to look at his Twelve Fifty and his Two Nine Five. All correct. He gets back to the Cliffhaven with an hour to spare, well satisfied with this ticket-of-leave facet of his new life.

Monday is the day for bathing. Would that it were in the sea itself, but it has to be in a town swimming pool. This morning, after rifle drill under a grilling sun, Webland and his mates are taken in to Coastington to this great pool, fully fifty yards in length, which about thirty of them have to themselves. The remainder take shower baths. All bathe naked, which makes it doubly refreshing, and Webland notices that Shag is a singularly good performer, and wonders why that should be.

The lads are again complaining about the feeding in the billets. Webland gets just about enough to eat at the Cliffhaven by packing up with slabs of bread, and the Welshmen down the road joke sourly about the risk of bread poisoning. The C.O. is concerned about it. He had visited the one o'clock meal about ten days ago to see the conditions for himself, but since that is the one good meal of the day, no good came of the inspection. He asks Webland now what he thinks of the feeding and Webland advises him to call at the Welshmen's billet during the evening meal. This he does and is annoyed at the scarcity; so some improvement may appear.

The next step on the way to a commission comes sooner than expected, when Webland is ordered with four others to report to the Group Captain in Coastington at nine o'clock next morning. As before, he is put in command of the little party, given the bus warrants and away they go to the long wait and the short interview. The applicants for R.A.F. commissions that he has come across seem generally to be rather a selfish type, or at least not concealing their air of being a cut above the commonalty. In this lot are a provincial insurance broker, a young engineer, a commercial traveller and a burly Scotchman from another Flight.

Attended by the good Squadron Leader, the Group Captain receives Webland quite urbanely and asks him if he has applied for a commission before and if not why not. Webland replies that to serve for a spell in the ranks must be a good thing in every way. There follow one or two questions about his past and whether Intelligence, Administration, or an Adjutant's job would suit him best. Webland doesn't know, but on departing it is very clear that there's nothing to stop this commission coming through very soon now.

But on with the training. Don't let up. This new health is glorious and the *esprit de corps* inspiring. It is not uncommon to hear a recruit from one of the Squads protest that his Corporal is the best of all the Instructors.

Webland's Squad is discouraged, though, to learn that their Corporal Eves, who has only been with them a week, is to be posted to another Flight. 'So,' they say, 'we are nobody's babies once more; we are the orphan boys, the lost legion, the forgotten squad; and just as we thought he was turning us into the smartest lot in the Flight.' In not much over a month this spirit has been born and flourished, and Webland is glad to be part of it. He thrives on the work, he delights in the classless comradeship, and he sees and understands all with a new interest. Even the bayonet-fighting practice under the bloodthirsty Sergeant Daly, with the steel flashing in the sun, holds for him something of an animal emotion, puts him in mind of royal Bengal tigers, beautiful in their killing power.

Good-bye then, Corporal Eves. The Squad will remember your short time in command of them with gratitude, as well as your touching admonitions: 'If you recruits make a mess of things on passing-out day, it's us Corporals who take back the can.' This phrase about a can is new to Webland, but it will clang through his service life, along with the sillier: 'Sorry, Charley, but you've had it.'

The Squad has had it, had its Corporal, and henceforward must make do with any that can be borrowed from the Flight. Corporal Todd, a small, neat Scot from Galloway, already well-liked from a distance, takes over for the time being.

Webland, as Marker for his Squad, still leads the Flight when on the march and is Right Hand Man when all the hundred and sixty are drawn up in lines of three. He gets chosen for any odd job the N.C.O. wants done, and in compensation often finds himself excused small periods of duty. For instance, he is sent off to his billets to fetch his kit-bag, underclothes, pullover, greatcoat, harness and packs for the Instructor to strap him up in front of the men and demonstrate how to pack and put the straps together. Reward: he gets rid of his rifle and is dismissed twenty minutes early.

The rifle movements are still imperfectly performed; the recruits have to shout the time and are rebuked for not doing it loudly enough: 'ONE PAUSE TWO PAUSE THREE PAUSE; ONE TWO PAUSE ONE PAUSE TWO!' Here's another chance for Webland, who has long since developed the power of his voice in the clatter of works machinery. It peals like Clara Butt's above the chorus for about half an hour until the Sergeant's itself gives out.

To signalize his heightened confidence Webland thinks he should get his Coronation Medal ribbon stitched above the breast pocket of his uniform. He has noticed one or two of the older airmen wearing a long service, police, or highly commended ribbon, and Corporal Cowley assures him that according to King's Regulations a man can be court-martialled for not doing so. In the face of several of his companions' last-war ribbons and one George Medal, he feels that to wear his souvenir of the day in 1937 when he had shown people to their seats in Westminster Abbey is almost impudent. But he decides to wear it for the last week of training and amuse his mates by pretending that it has just been presented to him by the C.O. for his exceeding smartness.

Once more Corporal Cowley, the rock of Cliffhaven, has received instant notice to proceed to the north on another course lasting three weeks. This means that Webland will be gone before his return and will almost certainly never see him again. Over their raisin pudding and custard this evening Mr Bolt and Webland sit in deep gloom, mourning their friend and guide of these past co-billeted weeks. Next morning at six-fifteen Webland cooks sausages for Corporal Cowley and himself, puts the kettle on, toasts the bread, and tries to show his gratitude as they exchange photographs and bid one another a warm farewell before parade at seven-fifteen.

Words of praise the previous day had been most heartening. Walking back with some of his mates after dismissal at five-thirty, Corporal Todd had called out: 'A/C

Webland!', and Webland had doubled back. The Corporal asked him how his application for a commission was getting on, and then conveyed to him, in his attractive native accent, how he had watched him trying all the time and what a capital thing it was for people like him to go into the ranks, and that if he continued in that style he would make a first-rate officer. The Corporal said that they had had some of Webland's type, by which he evidently meant folk with more money than most, and that they generally made no effort at all and seemed only concerned to demonstrate their fancied superiority. Moreover, he added, many officers who were in command didn't know their jobs and weren't thought much of by those below them. The recollection of these generous words restored some of Webland's lowered spirits.

If these Corporal Instructors were not good-hearted men what a hell could be this introduction to military life. There is not one among this Flight of N.C.O.s who is not a man of quality and some of more than average charm. There is Corporal Sowerby, for instance, once a traveller for a textile firm, who asks Webland how he likes the R.A.F. Webland cannot deny that so far he likes it much better than he had thought he would. Corporal Sowerby says that what he likes about it is the wonderful comradeship which you never get the like of in civilian life. They agree that it must have something to do with equal unfairness to all, hardships, jokes, privileges and perhaps later, danger, equally shared. That kind of comradeship, Webland thinks but dare not say, is alone reward enough; half-way to being in love, in a minor key, and without the anguish; what the French call *l'amour sans ailes*.

The Squad has now got so far as actually shooting with the rifles that they've swung and smacked about their bodies for so long. Webland has been looking forward to this, for he has shot since he was a child, and, though never a crack shot, he knows he will do fairly well. Firing on the range in details of fourteen, he finds himself next to a rather dozy lad in his own Squad. 'The great thing to remember, Fulton,' says Webland, 'is not to put any of your shots on my target.' He has seen it happen too often before.

They fire the first five shots for grouping. When the targets are examined Webland's is blank and Fulton's has ten holes in it. Mortified enough at his own folly, he is more so at having spoiled his neighbour's target. Fulton is forgiving and both await the Corporal's judgement. Webland says: 'Don't say anything to me about this, Corporal. I know it's unpardonable.' The Corporal merely looks pained, awards Fulton 20 out of 25 for grouping, and Webland, justly, nought: a proper penalty for overconfidence. Once return to drill, however, and his three billet mates, Stan, Ted and Bill, who alternately praise and tease him, will soon restore his self-respect.

Stan, the van driver, ugliest, bulkiest, jolliest of recruits, is the leader in the badinage. He calls Webland 'the Corporal's Flanneller'. At other times he says: 'Oh, you take the cake, Webland, easy. There's no one to touch you.' All are delighted to learn that he has had the heels and toes of his boots shod with steel, and wonder what sort of a crash he will stamp with for the last week of training in front of the Chief Drill Instructor, an exacting and unpopular Warrant Officer, the terror of the Wing. 'If they want bullshit they shall have it. Anyway,' he adds in an unusual mood of irresponsibility, 'I hope it rains like hell for the rest of this week so that we can get off drill.'

'Oh, Webby, you *are* slipping; you who was always so conscientious.'

But there's no slipping. He is still the Corporal's pet and the Squad's pride; and that afternoon he is singled out again. This time the Flight has marched off in column to the left instead of the right, so 13 Squad is at the rear and Webland in the last file of all. As it sometimes does, the step is going badly. Corporal Sowerby bellows above the crunch of boots: 'Can you run, Webland?'

'Yes, Corporal!'

'Then for Christ's sake run to the front and take the place of the leading man. I shall weep if they go on marching like this.'

This kind of thing, Webland thinks, is becoming so conspicuous that he wonders whether he is not being treated with some favouritism. So long as his mates don't really think so he finds it not disagreeable. But it is a bit disquieting. Yesterday the same Corporal had called out: 'Webland, change places with that man on the flank. He's too bloody slow!' And at bayonet practice with Sergeant Daly, to the whole Flight: 'Form up on Webland! Double up now!' (A blow in the solar plexus from his great fist, thinks Webland, would make anyone double up.) The men must be getting sick of the sound of his name. Yet no one seems to mind; and Stan, Ted and Bill, continue to chaff and to rejoice.

Little George, the old cockney sweat, whose tongue from the first day had never ceased from uttering graphically pictured filth, is becoming quite a friend. Having been ten years with the Royal Navy, no wonder he was pretty well browned off at being pushed around as a common recruit in the early days. But when the N.C.O.s find out that a man has served before they treat him with some consideration. George can look after himself, and he and Webland much enjoy their talks about their so different lives at home.

It is not quite so with Shaggy. He, if he is to keep out of trouble, needs watching. Webland, who has felt an initial aversion, born probably of fear, from this young jail-bird, is now really fond of him and wants to encourage him. This sentiment is understood by Shaggy, who reciprocates with a civility he doesn't show to everyone. Not that he is nasty to others, nor they to him. They treat him as a joke, which in a way he is, though a sad one, as he mutters out of the side of his mouth with many a wink and jerk of the thumb. But now he confidently comes to Webland, or Webland goes to him unasked, for help with his equipment and other troubles; and this is often. It is a relationship from which both profit.

Alas, though, for Shaggy when he is out of Webland's range, as when he irked the fearsome Sergeant in the unarmed combat training. The Sergeant has taken a slight liking to Webland; and well it is that he has, for he is a dangerous fellow to cross, and a few weeks ago, it is said, broke four fingers of an airman's hand. You might get the same, he warns, if you resist the tricks he is demonstrating. Thick, lewd and illiterate, he has somehow come to recognize Webland by sight and name, and so far from despising his spectacles and namby-pamby accent, he nods his approval at his ferocious snarls and oaths at bayonet practice, which by a measure of play-acting Webland has raised almost to a pitch of hysteria. Dale says that evidently they both feel the same way about the Boche. He hates any form of gentleness and appears to lose his temper with his pupils, swears at them, snatches off his cap and hurls it at them; but never at Webland, whom he sometimes singles out for demonstrations, and whom, if he has to correct him, he corrects with unaccustomed patience.

But with Shaggy it is far otherwise, for he is very strong, if more elegantly built than Sergeant Daly, and Webland dislikes the way they come together in this game of hand-to-hand fighting. Apparently Shaggy doesn't understand that he is not meant to resist these grips; instinctively he meets force with force, and very nearly gets badly hurt. The Sergeant curses his folly, Shaggy is released muttering grimly, and to everyone's relief the engagement of Titans is at an end.

He explains to Webland who has asked: 'Shaggy, why on earth didn't you give way like the rest of us?'

''E troid ter kick me in the cobbers, see? But Oi sor wot wos comin' and put me leg up quick, loike this . . .'

Certainly he got a nasty crack on the knee from the wrestler's boot. It is hard to please this Instructor, for the lads don't enjoy being called 'Cissies' and 'Chorus

Girls', yet are savaged if they get over keen. But they pick some fun out of the ferocity. 'To the stomick, POINT!' and: 'Fix 'im up in the goolies' are two phrases that are much relished; and when, in the middle of a verbal description of foul warfare, Daly pauses on an interrogation: 'Then what d'yer do?' they love to roar back: 'Kick 'im in the goolies!' And that becomes for a while a catchword in the Squad. When in doubt, 'Kick 'im in the goolies.'

Once again they are marched to the rifle range, this time for a kind of sweepstake shoot for all the recruits stationed in the town. A penny is demanded of each man and the winner will pocket about eight pounds. Webland, lying next to Jenkins, is dismally mindful of the last time, when he had put all his shots on young Fulton's target. A demon of a notion prompts him to suggest that Jenkins shall shoot at Webland's target and Webland at Jenkins's. This is agreed. When the targets have been shot at and assessed, Jenkins is declared the best shot among all the recruits. He cannot however claim the prize until he has done a final shoot-off against a Flight Sergeant, reputed to be a champion shot.

'All right,' says Jenkins whose shots on Webland's target had shown him to be a most unsteady marksman, 'let 'em all come.'

Whether the Flight Sergeant's nerve failed him, or whether from some other motive, no one knows, but he approaches Jenkins and suggests that they should split the eight pounds between them. Webland doesn't need to advise him to accept the offer.

That evening at six-thirty supper a message comes from the Orderly Room at Headquarters that they need a recruit who has done over four weeks' training to report at once for a twenty-four hours' turn of sentry duty. Webland volunteers, is helped into his harness and overcoat by his three grateful billet mates, gobbles a dish of food, grabs some sandwiches rapidly made by the thoughtful cook, mounts his bicycle in the dusk and presents himself at H.Q. for this fresh experience. The N.C.O. in charge turns out to be Corporal Driver: old friends, he and Webland, from that first shameful day on the rifle range.

There are five other sentries from other Squads, among them an electrical salesman and a footman to be trained as a batman. Two hours of duty and four hours of rest is the programme. Webland and another take up their posts at eight o'clock thirty yards apart. The night is starry and cool. They stamp up and down, chat and separate. When the moon rises, their bayonets flash silver; their rifles crash faintly as they slope and order them; the only other sound is the far roar of the sea. With no enemies about Webland enjoys the romance of it, which is little more real than those childish K.R.A. night operations under Roland. The rifle is rather heavier, that's all, and could mean real business.

The only unusual event of the long night is reported by a doleful-looking sentry named Stranks, who declares that he only had to issue one challenge of 'Who goes there?' This was to a noise in the bushes, from which issued an Airedale dog who then cocked his leg against Stranks's rifle. 'Pass water, friend!' said Stranks.

In the darkest four-hour period between ten and two Webland listens to Corporal Driver's history and philosophy. The Corporal has decided that he is an Old Sweat with no flies on him. He is barely twenty-seven and has served but a year in the forces after having been a school-teacher in London. He cannot understand why Webland insists on being, as he terms it, 'so bloody conscientious'. Webland has neither the heart nor the ability to explain.

'It doesn't pay in the Services, you know, Webland . . . you have got to look after Number One. . . . There's one way to get on in the Raff, and that's . . .'

'I know,' Webland breaks in. 'Crawl up people's back-sides.'

'You got it *exactly*!' The Corporal's eyes shine with delight at this recruit's prompt understanding.

There follow many greasy tales of how N.C.O.s get their stripes, as it were a nightmare volume of new Just So Stories. Also an effort is made by the Corporal to correct Webland's old-fashioned use of words by teaching him the vernacular. He already knows that he ought to say 'Ta' for 'Thank you', 'Ta-ta' or 'Cheero' for 'Goodbye', 'O.K.' for 'All right'. Now he should know that a recruit is an 'erk', a 'prog' or a 'rookie'; hospital is 'dock'; your head is your 'crust' or your 'loaf'; boasting is 'shooting a line'; prison is 'the glass-house' or 'jankers'; and many many more. This is good of the cynical Corporal, but he seems to enjoy giving information. After all, he was recently a school-teacher, and may yet be again; if so, Webland thinks, we should be rearing some hardheaded little scholars in North London after the war.

In spite of the absorbing interest of the conversation Webland, lying on a bunk in his uniform, drops off to sleep for about three hours, and at eight o'clock, in the surprising way things happen in the Service, he is told he can go, ten hours before he expects to. Is this favouritism again, or has the regular sentry reported for duty? Do what you're told and don't ask questions; and be grateful for this chance to have an afternoon nap on your bed at the Cliffhaven.

Later, in the brilliant evening sunshine, he sits for longer than usual in the little garden fronting the cliff walk, polishing his four boots and much missing the company of Corporal Cowley. They had used to sit there after duty, polishing, and chatting, and watching the passers-by, and exchanging quips with the A.T.S. girls setting out in twos and threes on their feminine excursions. This is when both Webland and the girls are most dependent on the absent Corporal, for Webland has no charm for them, nor back-chat. Today very few parties smile at him. One girl peeps over the hedge, sees the boots and says: 'Spit on 'em.' A pair, hoping perhaps that someone better may emerge from the billet, stay for a few minutes' chat. To his surprise they praise

their officers. 'Lovely they are, and perfect ladies, really.'
He had thought A.T.S. would be cats in such matters;
an ignorant, masculine notion.

It gets cold quickly now when the sun sets, for it is
mid-October. It is also the last week of the course. At
last, too, Webland's flayed body has ceased to fret.

Next day comes the rain. This adds to off-duty labours
of valeting. The waterproof camouflaged capes are good
so far as they go. Stan says: 'Me shoulders and feet's dry,
so I'm O.K.' But the rain plays hell with trouser creases.
It also runs down one's neck. Sergeant Vestry announces
that all lost creases must be restored to an edge that he
can shave with, for the adjutant's inspection in the morning. This means ironing on the kitchen table, when it can
be got hold of. Stan, Ted and Bill will no doubt show the
way. Mere soaping of the insides of the trouser legs, as
hitherto, putting them under the mattress and sleeping
on them, cannot produce that razor crease.

The C.D.I. is working on the Flight now, as he does
on each one in its final week. His second taking of them
finds him in better mood and them in better step, and he
dismisses them without threats. Only three times does he
roar: 'Fetch that man out and take 'im away!' With
a sharp bark he aims at Webland on the right of the
line: 'Wot's the 'quivalent army rank to a Squadron
Leader?'

'Major, sir,' barks back Webland.

So far so good. Nerves are tautening, though. No more
tea and buns are allowed at morning break. Instead, men
sit in the gutter at the roadside smoking and grumbling,
for they aren't allowed to leave the vicinity: a needless
rule it seems. All work is gearing up in speed and strict-
ness. Webland can take it and like it. Only four more
days to passing out.

The rain has made a shapeless clout of the men's
trousers; but what Webland hopes happens. His mates
all seem to be natural valets, washing their clothes in cold
water and hanging them on strings across their bedrooms.

Ted deftly irons Webland's trousers for him while he watches, praising the work the while.

In a downpour next morning, the Adjutant inspects the Flight and finds one or two pairs of boots not up to standard; not Webland's though. At bayonet-fighting practice Webland's lunges and growls and oaths have been so savage that Sergeant Daly picks him and a few others in the Flight to be in the front rank for passing out before the C.O. Most of the men are too timid and forgetful, but Webland has managed to thrash himself into an artificial frenzy. It is plainly what is wanted, and he feels as fit as a prize-fighter, his weight now, at 165lb., a stone less than on the day of his call-up.

It seems to be the custom to hold a what-ho party on the night after passing out, and Shag is looking forward to it more than most. He says to Webland: 'Are yer comin' along to our bit of a how-de-do on Monday night?'

'You bet I am, Shaggy.'

Then, mindful of the care Webland has taken to save him from being a discredit to the Squad, he says:

'I think you'll 'ave to adopt me, Webby, after the war.'

'When I'm a millionaire, Shaggy, you shall be my gamekeeper.'

After the Adjutant's inspection Sergeant Vestry announces that the best Squad has been judged to be No. 13, which surprises the Orphan Squad, having Shaggy and one or two others to be concealed in the depths of it. But there is much pleasantry and leg-pulling afterwards with the Corporals and the other Squads, and no malice.

After lunch the C.O. watches passing out at bayonet-fighting and unarmed combat. It has been arranged that Webland with three others is to do a special performance in front of the Flight. One man has to search a Jerry in a roughish way, another to break a stranglehold on his throat, and Webland to creep up behind a sentry, hurl him to the ground, and in the Sergeant's sinister words 'fix 'im up'. A brave recruit has volunteered to be mauled. All goes well. The volunteer is called out. Sergeant Daly, pretending to pick a man at random, points to Webland, whom he knows well by name: 'Come on you: the tall chap!'; and out he doubles. 'Fix 'im up.' It is all managed without pain, and Webland excels himself in ferocity, appearing to kick the falling sentry in the goolies followed by a lethal hook to the jaw when he's down.

Afterwards, Corporals Driver and Todd chaff him: 'You *are* a tough guy, Webland; or a rough one.'

'No milder creature walks this earth.'

'Says you!'

A new rumour spreads that some are to be posted immediately, and that there will be leave for those who stay. Stan is disgusted because he has heard he is off to the west coast of Wales instead of close to his dearest London. Shaggy and about ten others are being sent to various stations without waiting for the final parade before the Group Captain on Monday.

Volunteers are called for to go to the Armoury and clean the rifles and bayonets to be used for the parade. Only Webland and Ted step forward from their Squad, so four others are seconded by order. The good-natured footman from another Squad cleans beside Webland and tells him how much he liked his life among fourteen servants in Belgrave Square under such a nice butler. He says he can't help pitching into any work in sight and is much looking forward to becoming a batman. Webland silently hopes he gets an officer worthy of him.

In the Naffy that evening a few of them join Shaggy, who is discovered bandying words with a girl behind the counter. He will miss his bit of how-de-do next week, for he really is off to his new post in the morning. They all suppose that he has no money, so they stand him drinks. Putting his hand on Webland's shoulder, in a unique expression of *esprit de corps* he announces: 'Tell yer wot, Monty boy'; he often calls Webland after his father's well-known first name: 'we got the best Marker of the lot in our Squad, ain't we, Bill?' Bill agrees that Webland had pulled the Squad along fine. Shaggy, of course, doesn't care a fig for the drill, but he feels friendly, senses the atmosphere of pride in not dishonest work well done, and lives by what he calls his filbert. To have been acclaimed by a mutinous ex-convict as his own admired representative of discipline ought to be Webland's highest certificate for a commission.

'Good-bye, then, Shaggy. All the best.' And God help you, wherever you're going, with perhaps no other pal to get your cap and belt straight, to jolly you along and keep you out of mischief.

On Monday morning, to the disappointment of the C.O., it is learnt that the Group Captain can't come and inspect what is said to be the smartest Flight to be seen at Cadstone for some time. Webland, as Right Hand Man of this fine Flight and Marker of the best Squad in it, is disappointed too. But out they all pass, from recruithood into airmanship, C Flight dissolves, and those who remain become Pool Flight and await events.

A further rumour strikes at pride and spirits when it is believed that no leave is to be granted unless for exceptional cases of business or distress. Webland has received a command to dine with the C.O. that evening, so he may discover the truth of it. He is, moreover, relieved that this engagement will excuse him from attending the party in the Naffy when he would have had to drink too much and then probably been sick.

The C.O. gives Webland his leave pass for seven days, starting on the following day. The others also get their leave passes in batches throughout the week. A collection of cash, according to custom, is made for the N.C.O.s, and Webland subscribes with gratitude, yet wondering whether it conforms with King's Regulations. No one minds about that. But, on his return, what does seem rather strange is that most of his friends had been required to purchase their passes for ten shillings each from the Sergeant wrestler. Is this also according to custom? Webland's pass cost him nothing; what's more he had obtained a free dinner in the giving of it. He is thankful not to have been faced with this scale of privileges, and not best pleased at seeming to have been preferred in the matter of leave.

On leave with a free third-class railway ticket, he allows himself the luxury of a first-class carriage by virtue of his director's pass, which he has had sent from home. The ticket collector may not have expected it to come from an aircraftman's pocket, but he acknowledges its virtue.

Returning from his leave through London, Webland calls on an old friend, a member of the Government: he who had warned him against joining the ranks. There he learns, without asking or even wanting to know from any such source, that the Permanent Secretary to the Air Ministry, who, contrary to Webland's wishes, had been told by some well-meaning friend about his circumstances, had received his commission application and was attending to it. This news put him into two moods: one of satisfaction that he would soon be an officer, and one of annoyance that his career should be meddled with by any influential fingers. Let them leave him to climb his own ladder. He had told them all so at the start.

Arrived back at Cadstone, he discovers that, so far as being needed goes, he could have stayed at home a few days longer; for there is nothing to do but wait to be posted for his technical training, which is said to be starting on the 4th November. It is now the 29th October.

All but fourteen of the Flight are on leave or already posted, and it's hard to find out what has happened to whom, or which of his friends he will ever see again. Arriving outside the Cliffhaven and feeling despondent after leaving his family at home, the rigour of return is softened by two familiar Welsh voices: 'Is that Mr Webland?' 'Are those my old pals?' And off come woolly gloves for hearty handshaking and gabbled news. With much gossip the six weeks old machinery clicks back into gear and spirits are somewhat lightened. Ted and

Bill have left now, though, with never a chance of saying good-bye. But Corporal Cowley is back from his course and the Cliffhaven will be a better place for that.

Jenkins has had an odd occupation while Webland has been away; not so much odd in itself as in its implication. Remembering his manful reluctance to pay paper and string money on the first day at Glanville, Webland is full of curiosity to learn what he has now uncovered. Out it all bubbles in Jenkins's gay raconteur's style. He and one or two of his friends had been dispatched to unload coke from a railway truck at Coastington on to a service lorry. Interested to find himself ordered to shovel the coke into bags and to separate the weights into 18 cwts instead of the more usual one ton lots, he had started asking simple sounding questions. A younger Corporal had confided at last that the balance of the stuff was to be sold for the benefit of the N.C.O.s, and that the Sergeant was reckoning on making a £30 weekly addition to his income. The Corporal had said, 'We've got to live, haven't we?'

A short new life begins: a life of fatigues and dodging fatigues. George, the sailor, swims more closely into Webland's circle now. He sees no joy in digging others' gardens, helping the dentist, or scrubbing the Naffy floor, and he teaches Webland how to loaf about, drinking cups of tea and chattering with the old N.C.O.s, themselves browned off while waiting for a fresh Flight to come in. He takes him on a bus to the cinema, arguing that, since no one knows what to do with them, they might as well find their own occupations and save everyone trouble.

It is a strange chumship, brought about by forlorn circumstances. Webland is interested in George's quick intelligence and resourcefulness, while George is much entertained by what he calls Webland's 'dry way'. Ten years ago this small cockney had been a boxing champion of the Mediterranean Fleet, though why as an engine-room artificer he had left the Navy he has not revealed. Perhaps it had something to do with his knocking down of a haughty Midshipman who had given him an order in a way that he resented.

As confidence grows George tells Webland that he and others had at first looked on his la-di-da-voiced new friend with some lack of esteem. The wrestler Sergeant, for instance, had remarked to George that this fellow looked a bit dim, but in a few days had revised his opinion; to which George had replied: 'You ought to see 'im drill with a rifle.' George explains that the general view of the poorer classes towards a toff is that he must be a cissy; they look upon him with pitying toleration. Webland is glad he wasn't aware of that at the start.

A third unposted airman from the Flight has joined George and Webland in the few fatigues and many cups of tea. He is a violinist from Scotland, named Adam, and as much out of place in the R.A.F. as a nightmare could devise. He is borne up by his humour and commonsense, but he should never have been cast to do manual labour in this discordant band. His artistic nature and his mock bewilderment by military life appeal to Webland and make a good balance to the company of the artful George. Both men tell tales of horror and bravery in the bombings of their separate cities, and both evidently deserve George Medals.

For the last day or two the ill-assorted trio stick together in the to and fro of waiting; to the Naffy, to the pub, to each other's billets, and to such duties as they cannot sidestep. As rapidly as ever the unjust M.O. gives what is left of the Pool Flight a last medical inspection, called short-arm or F.F.I., which stands for Free From Infection; and there's no more trouble over anything N.Y.D. for Webland this time.

On the last evening George gives what he calls a bit of a do at a small hotel along the front. He is to be posted to Gloucester; Webland, Adam and about a hundred others to stations north of London. So it's good-bye, comrade, again.

Not looking forward to the do, but anxious not to let

George down, Webland leaves his billet that evening at eight o'clock, walks for half an hour, and shoves his way into the Saloon Bar packed with airmen and civilians in a fog of smoke which stings the eyes like tear-gas. George's delight at his arrival is ample reward, as he nervously introduces him to his two young ladies, three airmen and a commissioned Warrant Officer in the Royal Navy. In spite of his former protestations of being unimpressed by any hereditary rank, he allows himself to announce to the Warrant Officer that this is Lord Webland's son.

Webland is still more glad that he has made the effort to attend when he observes that, of the fifty or so men whom George had pressed to roll up, only the Flight Sergeant, one of the Corporals, Adam and another airman have done so. Drink after drink goes down, and Webland, asked what he'll have, achieves some distinction by saying: 'Mine's a Power Dive', a name he has only just learnt from Corporal Cowley as being a fashionable drink up at the station he had come from in Yorkshire. The Power Dive is merely stout and ale mixed and has no power at all. While others lower about four or five pints, he contrives to sip his way through a bare one and a half. Each takes his turn at paying nine rounds of drink, and the cost to Webland is four shillings and eightpence.

At this stage an unknown middle-aged civilian takes over the whole financial burden. He had been watching from a far corner and had been overcome by the fumes of patriotism at the sight of lads in uniform who looked as if their incomes couldn't stand this rate of consumption. This is a great relief to George, whose generous instincts are seldom supported by the cash with which to gratify them. In fact he has often found that he has to borrow from his guest in order to treat him.

The smoke grows thicker, the talk louder, the toasts more devoted, especially when George proposes 'The Royal Navy'. A piano, played by an airman who might have been a wizard at bayonet-fighting but had been taught neither how to get his foot off the pedal nor what his left hand should do to ground the faulty octaves of the right, resounds without pause until the dim lights are put out by the landlord, when it is 'Time, ladies and gentlemen, *please*'.

Adam and Webland walk back to their respective rooms, coughing and blinking and marvelling at folks' ideas of a pleasant way to spend an evening. The music must have been most distressing to Adam's delicate ear.

Next morning George is anxious to know how they had enjoyed the do. He declares that he's full of Dive Bombers, but it seems that he hasn't a very clear memory of either the Power Dives or the latter part of the evening. He bids his two recent chums a warm farewell and all the best; and that's the last of George, whose name was never George but Reg; a remarkable character, with his old discipline and love for the Navy, his independence, his scrounging, his obscenity, his pluck, his many talents and wits, and his way with strangers.

No sooner that farewell than farewell too to Cadstone, farewell once more to Corporal Cowley and to the Cliff-haven and its inhabitants. Heave-ho, then, with the kit-bag and small valise to join his posted mates at H.Q. for the long train journey to the next course.

'Come on now, get weaving!'

That's a strange phrase: no doubt from the looms of the North. And 'Get cracking!' Stranger still. Who originally got cracking? They never shout: 'Weave!' or 'Crack!' It has to be 'Get . . .' Anyway friendly Corporal Sowerby is the one who shouts it, and the hundred great-coated, haversack- and bottle-slung, kitbagged-and-case-laden airmen fall in for the march to the bus and the train. As a journey gift each man is given a paper bag containing a sausage roll, pastries and buns for the day. Some of the younger ones are in tearing spirits this morning, shouting and singing as wildly as children at a swimming pool. Cautious Webland murmurs: 'They'll be longing for the comfort of Cadstone tonight.' The old saying: 'You never know when you're well off' works truly in the R.A.F.

At the station the men are split into parties according to their destinations, fifteen with Webland getting into a reserved unequipped restaurant car for London. All these come from the old 14 Squad, chiefly Welshmen whom Webland knows and likes well, only himself being from No 13. His not to reason why. At London a lorry takes them across the city, past the window of the Board Room of his Insurance Office where he wonders if his colleagues sit today, to Liverpool Street. Having two hours to wait there, Corporal Sowerby allows him to leave the party and take a taxi to see his sister in Grosvenor Square, with a vow to be back in time for the train. This is trusting. What if he misses it?

There is another set of reserved compartments and in one he finds Jenkins, two Joneses, Corporal Sowerby, and, praise be, Adam. Adam and Webland being temperamentally well-suited had by that time tacitly decided to see the trials of the near future through together.

A pack of cards appears, with which some of them play '*Vingt-et-un*' which they call 'Pontoon' – a likely derivative – while the rest, in no very gay frame of mind, exchange an occasional sourish joke as being representative of the general cattle-like feelings engendered by military travel. Webland settles back in the corner and broods on the past two months.

He has learnt much of men and things. He has lived and worked with what might be called a cross-section of the middle and lower classes of the British Isles, and he cannot think of one among the hundred and sixty whom he hasn't liked and who hasn't apparently liked him. This is a marvel. Let him remember them, if only for a little while. It has been delightful and romantic; like being in the Foreign Legion, except that they are not very tough and are mostly respectable and home loving.

Take 18 Squad, for instance, manned chiefly by Scotchmen of the very best type, well built, better looking and more cultivated than those from the south; and 14 Squad, in which the Welsh, from Swansea to the Menai Strait, had soon formed a more or less exclusive fraternity, centuries of history having made them instinctively wary of the numerous, oppressive English. Yet, having sensed Webland's sympathy with their ancient land, they have welcomed him almost as one of themselves. They don't take kindly to the training, but none of them is notably unwilling, although Bryn Griffiths, formerly a contented fruiterer, is home-sick almost to desertion. Marching at ease in the first days at Cadstone he had taken from his pocket a snapshot of his wife and baby son and demanded of his neighbours whether it was right to abandon a home life of such tenderness for this kind of existence; and he had later announced in solemn tones, but with a gleam of fun in his unnationally blue eye: 'They'll neffer make an airman of me, Webland; *neffer.*' And obviously they won't.

Engineers, electricians, lorry drivers, undertakers, solicitors, shopwalkers, clerks, stevedores, seamen, tailors, commercial travellers, builders, scoutmasters, domestic servants, labourers, would-be missionaries, musicians, agents, grocers, secretaries, bank managers: all these, seen hitherto as figures in civilian days, have come to real life, been given hearts and characters, as it were in a magic toyshop. Webland is in the magic too, and these are all his friends. The spell will be broken, though, as in a fairy tale, and everything will pass, as these two months have passed. . . .

'Here's your bonnet,' says Adam, picking Webland's up from the floor. 'Just look at your tie. It's a tootal wreck.'

'Come on; get cracking, everyone!' Corporal Sowerby and the others are gathering their kit as the train pulls up at Swanton Junction.

A hooded, seatless lorry takes them to the aerodrome, jammed asparagus-tight, seeing nothing: 'So as we can't find our way back,' moodily intones one of the Welshmen.

Ejected at the camp Orderly Room, they shake hands affectionately with their ever dearer, now to be forever parted from, Corporal Sowerby, and turn in dejection to face what is coming.

'C Flight has been far the best and friendliest I've ever known,' the Corporal says. 'Old 17 Squad are going to have a reunion with me after the war and drink for a week.' He waves to them from the road as they go inside the gates. 'Oh, it's nice to be free! Cheero, chaps!'

'Cheero, Corp.'

5

Forgotten Men

Duke: Take thy commission.
Angelo: Now, good my lord,
    Let there be some more test made of my metal,
    Before so noble and so great a figure
    Be stamp'd upon it.
Duke: No more evasion:
    We have with a leaven'd and prepared choice
    Proceeded to you; therefore take your honours.
        SHAKESPEARE – *Measure for Measure*

Swanton has an aerodrome. This is good for airmen's spirits: to be able to see and hear the power of warfare and to be about to labour in uniform on the edge of it. But for the first few hours at a camp how drifting small a new arrival feels before his feet have felt the ground.

It is soon plain that there is not going to be much bullshit here, as the casual Corporal who takes charge of the new arrivals indicates. He conducts them to their lodgings, which is a double row of ten modern drab-coloured two-storey cottages within the camp boundaries, once known as the Married Quarters. They are equipped with fireplaces, a small coal-fired hot water system, and electric light fittings. But there is no fire for the water, no lamps for the sockets, and no furniture for the rooms except iron bedsteads and those square biscuits, three to each bed, with four blankets for covering.

At the sight sixteen expectant hearts sink lower towards thirty-two boots; and one heart reaches bottom as the

Corporal asks: 'Any friends want to be together?' Many
do: not Webland, though this was bound to come. He
has been too lucky already in having had that kennel
room at Cadstone to himself for his first two months.
Think fast, Webland. 'Yes,' he calls out boldly, without
having had time to do more than catch Adam's eye, 'me
and Adam.'

He thinks Adam is glad, as they clump inside one of
the tenements, select a room, and take possession. A
Leading Aircraftman, or L.A.C., already in occupation
upstairs advises them to move their beds from the chilly
room into the smaller kitchen, which, although at present
no warmer, has the advantage of a lock to the door, and
the prospect, if coal can be found, of getting a fire with
which to heat the tap water for the sink. There is not
much space, perhaps eight feet square, but by trying three
or four bed positions they manage to work out a pattern
in which the head of one or the other is neither under-
neath the sink nor in the fireplace, and the door can just
be opened.

They unpack on to bed and floor in facetious despair,
see that there is some coal outside, but no kindling wood,
then take their irons some 500 yards to the cook-house to
get something to eat. There they eat but cannot drink,
for the mugs have had to be left at Glanville long ago.
At Cadstone they had drunk from hotel cups and tumblers.

Having consumed the meal of potato, bread, margarine
and marmalade, they return to the Orderly Room for
leave to apply for mugs. There they are told that there
are no mugs; that in fact the only spare mugs around are
themselves: a quip which they pretend humbly to appreciate. Tread softly to begin with in a new place for fear
of what might spring.

Night falls. By sheer perseverance and unhelped, Adam
has procured a light bulb, and they set about trying to
warm the cold kitchen bedroom. Within half an hour
Adam has created a splendid fire from *The Times* and two
shovelfuls of wet coal; only there are no shovels: hand-

88

fuls, rather. He also teaches Webland how a newspaper can be plaited into a formidable kind of bludgeon, which can split the panel of a door and yet more easily an assailant's head; as effective as a bottle and more flexible. While they toil like dogs to wriggle comfort in their beds for sleep, the smoke from the coal blots each from sight. But the room is warming; and although by dawn the fire is dead, the water may still be tepid for the starlight morning wash in the sink.

Webland sleeps well that night, but Adam does not. He suffers too sharply from the stupidities of being forgotten, glared at, snubbed, suddenly ordered to undo things just done. He is a Roman Catholic and help may come to him. Webland is glad of that, for he will by no means disapprove of his companion's nightly practice of bedside prayer, which seems to both of them more than ever desirable.

Rising next morning at six-thirty in stinging cold they trudge across the camp to breakfast, carrying lidded saucepans, called mess-tins, to drink thick tea from. Following that comes a pseudo-parade, and for the next three hours the miserable sixteen fall in in threes, walk from one building to another getting pieces of paper signed by six departments, such as the Armoury, the Warrant Officer, the M.O., Pay Accounts, to establish the fact of their present existence in time and space.

Towards the end of this chain of events, Webland hears his name called out by a Corporal, who tells him to report at the Orderly Room. He reports, and finds himself furnished with a pass to London this very day for an interview for a commission with the Air Ministry at nine o'clock next morning, to the still friendly envy of his old Cadstone mates. But he is not released before having to undergo the inevitable F.F.I. This debagging welcome and farewell is beginning to lose its shame by its very familiarity. Good-bye and a good F.F.I. on leaving Cadstone. Greetings and a good F.F.I. on arriving at Swanton. It seems that, whenever an airman arrives at a fresh station, his duty is to report sick, sick or not, at 8 a.m. on the first morning to have the crutch of his body examined with a torch.

As he swings along the two-mile road to the railway station, with his bag for the night, his steel hat and respirator, his spirits rise again. After but one day at that dismal camp he has been picked out for the final interview at the source of commissions itself in London. A few days, or at most a fortnight, and he will have achieved his desire, and merited it a little too, strong in the knowledge that he knows about life in the ranks, at least from September to December, which is more than many officers can say.

On the half-hour's fast walk along the main road several cars and lorries have passed him, but he lacks the nerve to signal for a lift. Meanwhile life has not been too tough. He and his new friends have worked hard, cursed a little and laughed much on their training course. As for this place, the reception and the discomfort have not shocked so much as did the earliest days at Glanville; and they keep their spirits from passing right into the ground by the feeling of certainty that they will not be held there for long. The camp does not want them, there is no training to be done and nothing else of use to do.

At Kingsway the Selection Board doesn't spend much time on him. It seems to be assumed that he will be commissioned, the only question being which branch of the Service will be the most suitable. The word 'Operations' is mentioned: a wide sounding word with a medical ring to it. It might mean almost anything active.

'You can buy a book all about it,' says the President of the Board, 'just across the street. It's called *Readiness at Dawn*. Read it. That'll give you a good idea of Ops.'

Over the last hurdle, then, and the easiest of them all. There follows a medical examination in another building near by, passing fit in a category called A 4B, and so to the train back to Swanton and a chance to study the working of these Ops.

The book relates the adventures of an elderly junior officer at a Fighter Station near London during the first fifteen months of the war: interesting enough in any case, but far more so to Webland when he recognizes in a description of one of the officers controlling the Ops Room his close friend Frank Mead. Frank, now a Squadron Leader, has told him again that he is being asked for to come and work under him, as soon as he is commissioned, and it seems that the machinery is at last in motion. Well done, Frank. Better times are imminent. Meanwhile, back to good Adam, for whom he has bought a present of an enamel mug from London; back to a few more days of rank routine before liberation and translation into a one-thin-striped Acting Pilot Officer.

Adam is glad to have his room-mate back and to rejoice with him over his coming good fortune. Webland makes a successful fire in the manner taught him. He learns also how to darn a sock, skilfully demonstrated by Adam's violinist's fingers; most interesting: up and over, in and out, until across the hole stretches a tight weaving of fresh wool.

He likes to be among the first at the canteen for breakfast. With mug and irons, near the head of the queue, he shuffles past the serving counter, where the cook slaps out the food, and takes the two plates and mug of tea to a bench and table, all close-packed, when he gobbles the meal, returns the plates and hurries back to wash the mug and irons at his billet.

To their surprise the Cadstone sixteen are taken out to join in certain camp manoeuvres by transmitting messages on a radio telephone. 'Hullo, Blank calling Blonk, Blank calling Blonk. Are you receiving me? Over to you. Over.'

'Hullo, Blonk calling Blank, Blonk calling Blank. Receiving you loud and clear.' Dramatic stuff, this. Almost in the war now. A Sergeant looks in on Webland and Adam in their dug-out and stops to chat. Learning Webland's name, he says: 'Oh, you're the bloke we've heard of.'

Good or bad? Webland wonders. Judged by Cadstone standards, probably not bad. The Sergeant indicates that the choosing to go through the ranks had made a good impression on the lads. It's strange how fast the rumours race ahead. This confirms Webland's suspicion that he is an object of interest already, having noticed one or two men looking at him and murmuring together. A further mark of distinction is made after tea that day, when Webland, noticing that Morris of old 14 Squad seated next to him has no mug, offers him tea from his own, which Morris drinks gratefully. Afterwards Morris tells him that the man opposite had said to him:

'Was that Montagu Webland's son? Did he let you drink out of his mug? Blimey!'

It's impossible to infuse much comfort into the kitchen bedroom, and the weather is getting colder. The coal stock is soon exhausted, and a burst water pipe threatens to flood the floor; so after making a temporary repair, Adam and Webland decide to visit the Church Army hut, which is a room like a Village Hall, crammed with shouting, smoking, ping-pong playing soldiers, airmen and WAAFs, the whole with loud, invisible musical background.

In the long gaps between meals the chocolate ration comes in gratefully but chocolates can only be bought on a cigarette coupon. Webland, who doesn't smoke cigarettes, attempts to buy his weekly chocolate allowance of a 2½d. bar, but is told that he can't have it unless he buys cigarettes first. This seems to be a case for the chaplain to attend to, so next morning he calls on him above the Orderly Room, is heartily agreed with and is sent away with a promise that the injustice shall no longer continue. So it proves, and the rights of non-smokers are safeguarded. He gets his chocolate without cigarettes; but tobacco for his pipe he cannot buy, for at present there is none.

Is all the hard-taught drill at Cadstone of no account here? Each day at Swanton for the lost sixteen seems a day

wasted in useless odd jobs and standing about in the
passage of a building devoted to some kind of direction-
finding radio. They don't even march to the place, and the
attitude of the N.C.O.s is familiar almost to equality.
They are technicians, so it may be all right. But it seems
militarily unnatural.

Sunday comes with a morning Church Parade and a
band to march to: pleasant, if not stirring. But the drill is
not up to Cadstone standards, and two of the six Right
Markers on parade turn left instead of right about. No one
seems to mind very much; but Webland grieves for past
glories and wishes he and 13 Squad could show them how
to do it.

At eleven o'clock he is free to leave the camp on a pass.
He decides to call on a schoolmaster friend in the cathedral
town ten miles away. He must now learn to hitch-hike.
Getting a quick start at the gates in the back of an R.A.F.
lorry, he is taken two miles beyond his turning for Carchester. He walks back and along the right road for three-
quarters of an hour, until an Army truck picks him up for
another three miles and puts him down in company with
a trooper of seven years' service with the 17th Lancers,
also on his way to Carchester. Ten civilian motor-cars
ignore their signs before one stops and takes them on for
four hundred yards. But soon afterwards comes another
compassionate Army truck, and the game of getting there
is over.

Webland blesses his luck with his fellow servicemen.
The trooper had been as friendly as could be, as he
trudged along with his rifle and pack, while Webland
carried his respirator for him.

He said to Webland: 'Do you get on with the wife's
relations?'

'Yes. Very well.'

'I don't. The wife's brother's a conscientious objector,
but the wife's a real lady. She's grand.'

Then he told Webland how a month or two ago he
had met the very airman who had been reported in the

newspapers as having been given a lift on the road by Queen Mary in her car. She had given him £1 as well as taking him out of her way to catch his leave train. The airman was a rough cockney and had no idea who she was till the 'Lady in Waits' told him at the end. He is now, said the lancer, a converted and idolatrous royalist, protesting that Royals can't help being who they are and that anyone who says anything objectionable about them doesn't know what he's saying. The airman had tears in his eyes, said the lancer, as he spoke of what this Queen had done for him.

Back at camp that night Webland and Adam deplore the lack of coal and decide that there is nothing for it but to follow the general practice and take to crime. This means looking about in the day-time and picking up and pocketing or putting in their drinking-mugs any small pieces of coal or coke lying by the wayside, and after dark sneaking round the back of the cook-house with some larger container.

If only one's sleeping quarters were warm the life at Swanton would be quite pleasant, for plenty of latitude is allowed within the camp so long as you keep to the few rules. The water closet is clean and efficient. There are entertainments, or ENSA concerts, in the evenings; and yesterday Webland discovered a small, barish room called the library, where one can hire a book for a penny. In it were two tables, two armchairs, and a sofa on which was sitting a Negro soldier in a khaki overcoat. The other occupants were six airmen, another soldier, and, Heaven be praised, a sailor. What can sailors be doing here? And even more what can Americans be doing?

Webland has just witnessed a spectacle on the parade ground which took him back to an old scrapbook at home where was a sketch of Dreyfus being stripped of his officer's insignia in the sight of his comrades of the French Army. There at Swanton aerodrome, in front of the parade, a Sergeant Pilot was reduced to the ranks, his hat and coat removed, and given forty-two days' punishment. This is a sight that stirs the strangest emotions and Webland is aghast. When was he going to cry out, as Dreyfus did: 'I am innocent!' Even supposing the man to be trebly guilty, who could suppress his pity at this truly awful ceremony? Spectators said that he was an American. What had he done wrong? Had he broken faith or worked abominations to his aircraft? No one knew.

The days pass slowly for the workless. A little polishing of a floor, a little sweeping up, perhaps a chance of cleaning and oiling the Flight Sergeant's bicycle make up the day's useful occupation. No officers come near the Cadstonians, while all continue to wait and wonder.

Some coal has arrived at last: one hundredweight for three fires for a week. It doesn't look much, but that evening all the ten chimneys in the street of the married quarters are smoking merrily, and the lads look forward to a few warm evenings; especially so as Webland's fifteen mates have just been re-inoculated and will need to nurse their ensuing fevers. Why they omitted to jab Webland he doesn't know, but supposes that it is because he is so soon to become an officer.

One advantage of the Cadstonians' unwanted presence at Swanton is that a 24- or 48-hour leave pass will be not infrequent; and after less than a fortnight Webland and some of his lot are able to get home for a few hours. He, car-borne for so many years, now thinks nothing of walking two miles to the station carrying his bag to catch the 7 a.m. train to London. Missing breakfast is unimportant so long as one doesn't miss an hour of leave.

Returning two nights later, refreshed in spirit, he sets off along the road back to the camp conscious of two great boons, physical fitness and freedom from any responsibilities but those of obeying simple orders. Marching by what Samuel Pepys called 'brave moonshine', he feels a transcendent lightness of body and mind. And how grand are boots, heavy boots, for swinging the feet in easy rhythm! How far superior to shoes!

95

Not 'Shoes shoes shoes shoes,
            Slapping up and down again'
for Kipling or for Webland. The half-hour tramp seems
to pass in a jiffy.

Adam is back already and has made Webland's bed and
a good fire; but for an hour they join Davis, Griffiths
and Thomas in their room for a grumble, not without
laughter, at the horrors of service life compared with life
at home. Exclusive as they may be, they have admitted
Webland, and through him his Scotch room-mate, to
their fraternity.

Next morning, to everyone's astonishment, a job has
been created: a job for four men, though ten have been
detailed for it. This, Webland is told, is the R.A.F. method.
The job is to push a hand-cart round the perimeter of the
aerodrome and hit stakes into the ground. This is much
more amusing than hanging about in the radio room and
passage, where there are two seats to sixteen men and
nothing to do but read the newspapers and listen to the
music from the B.B.C.

Webland hopes the hitting of stakes will go on for
weeks, or at least until his call comes from the Air Ministry.

One day when they have taken the cart and the stakes
to the site for cable laying, there is no sign of the foreman,
so, it being a sunny morning, the stake hitters spend a
pleasurable hour or so watching the aeroplanes take off
and do what are called circuits and bumps. For Webland
at any rate it is a new and thrilling experience to be able to
view these deadly monsters so near at hand, and to feel
that he has an airman's right to be there.

That evening, he finds himself next to a forgotten man
at supper, whose story makes the Cadstonians' three
weeks old neglect seem trivial. This young man tells
Webland that he has been at Swanton for a year while the
Records Department had shown no sign of recognizing
him. His face is haggard and in his eyes is the look of one
who has seen strange visions. A year ago he was to have
been a pilot, but falling sick he spent a few days in hos-

pital. When he recovered he found he had missed his
chance. At first, he said, when week after week he was
expecting to resume his training course, which he was
half-way through, he was dreadfully brassed off – proper
cheesed off – fed up; then, as the months went by, he
settled down and was put to a clerical job in the Orderly
Room; but, now that Records have found him and are
hustling to repair the damage, he no longer cares what
happens to him. It is plain to see that he has lost all feeling,
all ambition, and is a mere automaton, content to plod,
quite without bitterness, through each day in this chronic
trance.

Some of the lads say that his is not the only case they've
heard of, and they are beginning to feel rather apprehensive lest something of the kind should happen to them.
Once more Webland has cause to thank his stars that he
has passed all the screens to his commission. Still, it is a
month now since the Cadstone course, and if things had
gone right their technical training ought by now to have
been almost completed.

At the radio room the following morning appears a
batch of about a dozen men from a Cumberland square-
bashing, to join the original sixteen from Cadstone. This
will crowd the standing space and the two seats. They
had arrived last night in time for supper – the usual soup,
bread and cocoa – having started their journey at 6.30
that morning with two sandwiches each, to find no place
to sleep in. Two Sergeants had called at the married
quarters at about half-past eight, flashing their torches
and asking if there were any spare beds about. 'That's the
R.A.F. way,' say the men, who are already beginning to
become cynical about organization; 'it's the System.'

Adam says his Roman bedside prayers this night more
earnestly than ever. Webland's spirits keep their level as
he thinks forward to becoming an 'Ops B' in what *Readiness at Dawn* calls 'the nerve centre of a Fighter Station's
being'.

He has cheerfully perpetrated two pieces of dishonesty.

He has discovered a telephone booth outside the camp which gets you through to your number when you put the pennies and sixpence in and returns them at the same time. He has also helped to steal some wood to supplement the dwindling coal. At the camp orchestral concert he appals Adam by saying: 'I wonder how many fires we could get out of that double-bass.' Air Marshal December has taught him to look at everything in terms of fuel. No wonder billeted soldiers burn gilt picture frames and Jacobean staircases.

Wellington boots have been issued to those hitting in stakes, of which the hitting in of two represents a full morning's work for each man. Webland's boots are two sizes too large and will soon destroy his socks by dank attrition. A junior Officer of the technical radio branch supervising the issue, when Webland suggested being given a size to fit him, replied: 'They'll be all right if you wear your football stockings.'

'Where are my football stockings, Adam?'

'Put away with your tricycle and teddy bear.'

Webland will have to send for some stockings from home. Meanwhile, struggle on; to the eternal sound of music. Everyone who thinks he and she can sing at all croons *fortissimo* all over the camp, and in the house opposite Webland's a WAAF does it out of her window night after night. What does it all mean? Happiness? Longing?

Two new rumours are afoot. First, there should be seven days' leave at or around Christmas, if there's no posting for training during the next four weeks. Second, two of them are to go at once to Coastington as witnesses in a Court Martial over allegations of corruption among recruits and certain N.C.O.s in C Flight at Cadstone. This makes the guilty ones feel nervous, but Webland considers the N.C.O.s to blame when they allow or induce recruits to bribe them. There are so many crooked things done all the time in the ranks that many cease any longer to distinguish theft from gift, bribery from honest thanks.

Webland and Adam discuss these matters as, with spade and pickaxe, they dig a two foot hole and string up a small radio aerial, watched by a Signals L.A.C. and four chatty officers of the 17th Lancers. And, by the way, what can the Death or Glory Boys be doing at Swanton Aerodrome? Adam guesses that their records Department have mislaid them. Odder things can happen under the System.

The two summoned to Coastington are Webland and Hickman, a dealer from the north whom Webland had known slightly square-bashing at Cadstone. So, with small kit in haversacks, respirators and steel helmets, they are lorried to catch next morning's train to London. There they part to meet again at the end of the journey. Webland, now quite unself-conscious in his aircraftman's uniform, travels down to Coastington in a first-class compartment with an elderly businessman. This man, not having enjoyed his meal in the tea car, complains of the great profits made by the railways under Government control, and doesn't Webland agree that it is perfectly scandalous? Webland answers: 'No.'

'Well, look at that forty-six million a year the Government are paying them.'

Webland says: 'Look at what that represents on the capital involved. Not much of a percentage, is it? The Government will do well out of the deal if the war goes on much longer.'

The man, not knowing within hundreds of millions what the capital of the railway is, raises his newspaper before his reddening face and speaks no more, thinking, no doubt, that you can't trust anyone these days. The aircraftman, like a hawk in lark's plumage, feels he has won an unworthy victory.

Hickman is waiting in the Railway Transport Officer's room at Coastington, and a Corporal takes them to an hotel which serves as the H.Q. of the Service Police. Prepared for any sort of vile and crowded accommodation, Webland is conducted to a private bedroom, with clean

sheets and towels, has a luxurious bath, and joins a crowd
of Corporals – all R.A.F. Police seem to be Corporals – in
a large room where they are playing ping-pong and
billiards. Hickman has been put to share a room with a
home-sick Corporal who shows Webland a picture by his
bedside of his baby son at home in Devon.

Webland wonders if he and Hickman are under some
form of technical arrest. They are told they must not
leave the building, presumably in case their coming evi-
dence gets tampered with. He cannot think why the
Police have picked out these two of all the Cadstonians,
but after some experience of the System he won't be
surprised to hear that they are to be locked up on some
mistaken charge.

The morning, however, brings no drama; only a few
questions from an Officer whom Webland takes to be an
Aacting Provost Marshal – he is still ignorant of many
ranks – and who explains that Webland had been sent for
as being a level-headed sort of chap, and did he know
anything about leave passes being bought and sold at
Cadstone? It is a relief for him to be able to state that he
can only repeat what had been told him by his mates on
his return from his own unpaid for leave.

Did he know of any similar cases of dishonest conduct?

He doesn't see any point in mentioning the collection
they made so willingly on behalf of dear old Sergeant
Vestry on bidding him good-bye; but the almost forced
tribute paid by nervous recruits into the squalid Corporal's
cap at Glanville ought not to be hushed up. So he has the
pleasure of sneaking to the Police Officer on that; and
the Officer seems grateful and says that he won't be
needed at the Court Martial after all.

Back again at camp, Webland is soon negotiating to
buy a small Ford car from a Sergeant, to replace his large
one at home which has already got damaged in the black-
out and is costly and unwieldy for his wife to drive. A
price of £55 is agreed and the shabby vehicle is his. He is
told that he may apply for petrol coupons for the purpose

of taking the car to his home. In order to ensure that there is no hanky-panky, the application has to pass through the offices of a Warrant Officer, a Flight Sergeant, an Officer commanding the Signals, the Adjutant, and a WAAF officer whose job it is to hand over the coupons. Waiting, saluting, asking, saluting, walking and waiting take up most of the day; but it is successfully done.

It is only after he has completed the process and examined and calculated his coupons and his mileage that he discovers something else that might interest a Provost Marshal. The Warrant Officer had asked him how many miles it was to his home. Webland thought about 120. In some forceful way, the details of which Webland couldn't recollect, the Warrant Officer had insisted that the mileage was in fact 200 and that he would issue coupons for that distance. Aircraftmen don't argue with Warrant Officers. The Warrant Officer then murmured something about Webland coming back after he had procured the coupons from the WAAF officer and handing over the surplus quantity to him. 'And don't tell anyone where you've been, see?' Webland with a 'Thank you, sir', went out and on with the business.

The incident vexes him and he consults Adam, who thinks that on no account should the cunning Warrant Officer advantage himself in this way. But what if he should seek revenge? It wouldn't be hard to wreak. It is decided to keep the surplus coupons and await results.

The Christmas leave rumour is taking shape. There has been a ballot for the hangers-about in the radio room. For the eleven married and with children there are to be nine granted leave. Webland and another fail in the draw. But really, it seems to him, things have gone so well that it's about time his luck did change; and although to miss Christmas Day at home is disappointing, it is almost better to store the pleasure in growing anticipation. Anyway, he has the petrol and the car and the leave to take it home. And this he accomplishes satisfactorily.

Soon after his return to camp from delivering the

unsightly machine to his startled wife, he is approaching the cook-house for dinner with one of his Welsh friends. The weather is still getting colder, he has no gloves and he shoves his hands in his trousers' pockets. A shout of 'Airman!' from a red-armleted Police Corporal pulls both up short. 'Do you mean me?' 'Yes, you!' The Corporal indicates the crime. Webland hadn't known that hands should not be pocketed during off-duty hours round about billets and cook-houses. The gentle Welshman, Griffiths – he who had once gloomily said: 'They'll never make an airman of me, Webland' – is shocked and full of sympathy. Webland makes light of it, but is nevertheless annoyed with himself over that lapse from smartness.

Next morning a Warrant Officer, not the coupon dealer, comes into the radio room. 'I want a clerk. Has anyone been a clerk?' Webland has just finished cleaning a bicycle. He volunteers, and spends an enjoyable day beside him at his desk copying out a list. The reward is a real chair to sit on.

Polishing his sixteen buttons and his cap badge, Adam that evening spills the bottle of Silvo over his tunic and through it to the skin.

The repair of this upset occupies the two of them for most of the evening, and Webland learns much about valeting from this very practical musician. He learns also how to clean his old and slimy sponge: a problem that used to be solved before the war by throwing it out of one of the back bedrooms to the chauffeur to use on the cars. He and Adam boil it on the fire in a mess tin, and after three boilings in changes of water all the old soap and dirt scum to the top, leaving the wretched object slightly heat-tanned and half the size, but as clean and springy as a young deer. If they had had some vinegar, Adam says, it would have come out as good as new.

Another day brings another job: bicycling four miles carrying a motor-car's starting handle to an Air Force house. This doesn't take long. In the afternoon Webland, Adam and a wireless mechanic drag the heavy hand-cart round the perimeter seeing to radio apparatus; the mechanic does the seeing, the other two the dragging. While dragging they amuse themselves by affecting north-country accents with plenty of swear words so as to be mistaken for long service technicians.

But, with no sign yet of being posted for training, all the men are getting browned off wasting their time at Swanton. And the quality of the food is becoming uncertain. On successive days Webland has raised a hawthorn leaf from his cabbage, a piece of india-rubber from his rice pudding and a lump of coke from his currant suet.

Most browned off are Jenkins and the two Joneses, Phil and Twankey. Sitting on the edge of Webland's bed under the sink, Jenkins tells Adam and Webland about their life at a neighbouring aerodrome they've been sent to work on. They have to sleep in a cow house with a concrete floor, on beds and biscuits, of course, but with filthy black old pillows; and they have to carry water in buckets a hundred yards round the farm buildings for their washing and shaving. They have a stove but no fuel, and they are told by the L.A.C. to steal it after dark from the soldiers' heap of coke near by. The first time they prowled along with their sack a soldier tried to prevent them, but Jenkins, judging him to be Welsh, spoke to him in his native tongue and he became entirely helpful. But Twankey, a fishmonger from Builth who looks like a melancholy pantomime dame and had volunteered for himself and the others to go to this place on the understanding that it was to be for only three days, sits every evening with his head in his hands moaning – and Jenkins's Welsh accent takes on a mournfuller lilt. 'It's all my fault,' says Twankey. 'I've brought you other two to this. I've a good mind to 'ang myself on the beam. I shan't do any work,' he says. 'They've brought us 'ere under false pretences.'

To make a treat Webland takes Adam into Carchester one evening for a bath in his hospitable friend's house and a dinner of pheasant, beer and wine at a restaurant.

After a glass or two of port Adam feels constrained to express his gratitude to Webland for his moral support during these past weeks. In a way, perhaps the two have been complementary, for Adam's humour and practical knowledge have been invaluable to Webland, while Webland's striking quality, Adam confides, is his restraint. Not much to that; and anyway it's probably just a matter of nerves, Adam being a sensitive artist and Webland very much less of one.

Not every restaurant welcomes airmen. At the rather refined public house near the railway station, for example, the host and hostess have treated Webland's polite inquiry about a meal with stark insolence. Officers mostly go there, and Webland has formed the impression that a higher rank or a large bank account would have discovered a more welcoming attitude.

Now comes another job: three days of dug-out life on manoeuvres. Uncomfortable as it is, it speeds the hours by its variety, and is better than lounging in the radio room listening to dance music. It is called 'standing-to'. Much of the time is spent trying to make up for lost sleep in a damp overcoat and blanket on a slatted floor. Adam loathes it.

The young soldiers they are associated with underground are a particularly good-natured lot. They present the two wet and cold airmen with a blanket and a leather jerkin, and gladly share their precious bread and jam and cheese and meat paste with them.

One of them used to be a grocer's boy in Bolton, one a tailor's cutter's apprentice, and one worked in the Japanese Embassy in Grosvenor Square. An elderly soldier is no less kind; he brings Webland a paillasse and some more blankets.

The airmen's job is not arduous, being merely a link in the mock warfare by means of a radio-set called a TR9. They don't know what it means or what they are linking, but they pass on messages as loud and clear as they can. The soldiers however, all soaked through with rain, have to turn out for guard duty after a day's sham fighting and an hour or so of shivering sleep. How patient they are, how cheerful, and how friendly, especially the youth who calls Webland 'Choom' at the end of every sentence.

The upshot of the seventy-four hours stand-to brings him more good luck. It has been rumoured that all the loungers at the radio room are to be sent to the neighbouring aerodrome. And it is true. 'All you men in here,' says the Flight Sergeant, 'get your kit and catch the bus at the Guard Room at ten o'clock.' Some of the permanent staff express their condolence, remarking that it is a bloody dump and that everyone dreads it like Siberia. Hearts sink. Starting for their billets they are called back and told that they are to stay behind after all. Hearts tremble. 'You, Adam and you, Webland.' It is discovered later that these two are judged to have operated the best dug-out radio during the manoeuvres, though all 'put up a damn good show'.

Griffiths, nostalgic as ever, makes an effort to escape. Unseen, he takes his kit off the lorry and scoots round to the back of the Signals building. The Flight Sergeant, noticing his absence, finds him. 'What the hell are you doing here?'

'Sweepin' up, Flight,' says Griffiths, vigorously working on the grass with a broom he had snatched up on the way. He is quickly brought back to his fate and the tumbrel.

Adam and Webland become messenger labourers to the Signal Section, and can spend more useful days dragging things round on a cart and fixing up aerials for the mechanics. They might learn something, too. It has been a good day. The rain has given way to bright frosty weather; Webland has been issued with a new shirt and has got his laundry back, clean and complete. But the main joy is that he and Adam are not being thrown out to the Bloody Dump. Such meagre blessings make a bountiful day for an untrained airman.

On the principle of 'Take your leave when you can or you may find you've had it', Adam is to get away for seven days to his wife a fortnight before Christmas. Being uncertain how to get his railway warrant and catch the 2.16 to Grimsby, he obviously needs Webland's inexpert help, so Webland procures the afternoon off to speed him. 'Trust me,' he says: 'I'll get you there. Everything will be all right.'

At the Guard Room, where the pass should be, no railway warrant is with it. They are directed to P. Staff. After twenty minutes someone comes and writes one out for him. During the wait they hear an Australian WAAF cursing Government and King. She will do anything, she says, to get out of the service, even to the enormity of having a baby. Since she is married to a pilot she might manage it without loss of prestige, though it's a somewhat ill-natured conception. Next appears a Warrant Officer acting berserk, calling out the Service Police to enjoy a morning's bullying of any and sundry passing by; all done with fearful oaths. This is just the kind of thing that shatters Adam's nerves, and today he is easy game for the Warrant Officer, not having closely buttoned his overcoat collar. There is no punishment, but he gets a verbal mauling. No one is more law-abiding than Adam, and Webland longs to tell the bully so, lacks the pluck and folly.

Escaped from that peril, Webland hails a milk lorry not far up the road, pops Adam in the front beside the driver, clambers among the churns behind, and they all fetch up three minutes' walk from Carchester station. Adam's luck is in, for although he's had no lunch, a W.V.S. canteen supplies them with sausage and mash, cakes and tea, all in perfect time for his train. Webland waves him off, as proud of the fulfilment of his morning's frantic boast as any man could be.

Poor Adam has been getting rather jumpy lately and his nerves are due for a rest. The eight-foot square kitchen-bedroom will be roomier now. Though Webland is fond of him, admires his character, and is grateful for his tidiness and other good domestic qualities, his absence for a week will mean some solitary peace. And he knows that, if he makes a muddle of things on his own and needs help, at least three roomfuls, two Welsh and one English, will bring him instant succour. Manifestly no N.C.O. or Officer will. What he has seen of his small section of the R.A.F. shows him that there is none of that daily close relationship between officers and men that is supposed to exist in the Army; no equivalent of the young subaltern having a body of men whom he's responsible for, knows by name, and whose comfort he must always secure before his own. The cavalry are said to do as much for their chargers. There used to be a word of command, perhaps still is: 'Make much of your horses!' Perhaps foot troops might do better if they heard occasionally: 'Make much of your men!' But it's very plain that no officer knows anything of these men's lives, in work or in billets; and that surely shouldn't be. Perhaps there are in effect two R.A.F.s: the air one and the ground one. Apparently there can be little wrong with the former; but as for the latter, Heaven help the lowly airman.

What specially annoys the men is when officers don't find time to sign pieces of paper for those going on leave. They let the papers lie about, while the owners of them chafe to get away and wonder why they can't – just for the want of the lifting of a pencil and a few seconds of signing a name. Every hour of leave is beyond price and to have it frittered in this way is torture to the mind. Webland has been told of men's embarkation leave, which should be always fourteen days, being whittled down to a bare forty-eight hours for no discoverable reason but muddling and neglect. No one responsible cares. Now, when Webland becomes an Officer. . . .

He has plenty of time to speculate upon his future as he sets about making his fire without Adam's guidance. At five o'clock laboriously he lays it: crumples lower paper loose; plaits upper paper tight; distributes his lips to the fire bars and puffs, on and off, until six. The wet coal begins to catch. More tending, rearranging, holding a newspaper across the fireplace to increase the draught. He is still maladroit. In this room the smoke blows down the chimney for an hour; then as the heat increases it goes up, though occasional wind gusts blow it down again. The fire exhausts its fuel supply at eight o'clock, but by that time it has fulfilled its purpose, and Webland has proved himself the master.

There is cleaning of muddy boots with a dinner knife, drying them in the oven with the socks, and polishing them. There are the buttons to rub bright, perhaps one or two to sew more tightly, darning socks and gloves. There is sweeping the room clear of yesterday's dust. There is boiling the water in his mess-tin for a shave. During all this, David Jenkins pays a visit from over the way, purely out of kindness because he knows Webland's room-mate is away. And he's not the only sympathizer, as Webland has had abundant offers of hospitality from other neighbours. For all this rotten idleness at Swanton, there's no sign yet that the Cadstone spirit of comradeship is degenerating.

It seems longer than three and a half months since these comrades first faced one another at the kitting depot. Jenkins reminds him of how they had shared a grim room that very first night at Glanville, when Webland had shouted in his sleep. 'Hector Macdonald' were the only words that could be recognized.

Jenkins chatters on with his tales of innocence and corruption: of how he was ordered to be a cook at the Bloody Dump and acted total ignorance, although he could cook fairly well. 'How do you tell when the potatoes are cooked, Sergeant?' 'How do you make gravy, Sergeant? With Yorkshire relish?' Of how one morning, when Webland was out with his hand-cart, the Corporal wanted an airman to ride his bicycle into Carchester and leave it there for the Corporal to return on that night. 'You take it, Jenkins.' 'How am I to get back, Corporal?' 'That's your affair.' 'But I don't know how to ride a bike,' which happened to be true, says Jenkins; but the strange thing was that not one of the other thirty-eight men knew how to ride one either.

His sympathy with Webland is a tonic. He says that it is scandalous how the N.C.O.s pick on Webland for all the dirty jobs. Webland hadn't observed this, but thinks if it is so perhaps the reason is that he is hoping to win his commission by never shirking. There had been a libellous column in some newspaper about Webland's father, and Jenkins assures him that all the men feel for him and are angry with the malicious journalist. With such comrades and such talk his spirits cannot sink for long.

After all, Webland is now offered the chance of going for his seven days' leave three days before Christmas instead of four days after. This is a teaser. Yet he must decide without delay, for there are only five days more till the 22nd. Let a coin decide. It does so. Heads! Home for Christmas he shall be.

Very much better settled, too, are his old comrades at the Bloody Dump. On a visit one evening across the way to the room of some lads from the north country where they made him share their spread of cake, apple tart, cheese and other delights such as Yorkshire and Lancashire folk know best how to provide, they tell him that they have hinted to those in charge that their Members of Parliament might be interested in their living conditions at the Dump; since when, they have been rapidly supplied with overalls, transport to and from their billets here, four miles each way, which they formerly had to do on foot, unless they chose to sleep in Twankey's cow house; and every Saturday they are to have free. They now consider themselves better off, since at least the food was always more palatable there, than Webland and Adam at the old radio room.

Webland is now managing well on his own and has finally mastered the fire. Deftly he fashions his newspapers, four of which he has to buy daily as tinder, into turbans and accordions, spatters last night's cinders on top with a handful of fresh coal, a touch from the cigarette lighter and up she goes inside five minutes. Still, the neighbours chaff him about the smoke his room contains and emits, and pretend the house is on fire; but that's the chimney's fault, not his.

Delayed by gossiping with Morris, who had looked in for companionship during Webland's evening wash, he is too late for the chocolate ration rush at both the Naffy and the Church Army, but at the latter place the manager goes behind and surreptitiously passes him a small packet of the precious stuff, saying: 'You must come along to Toc H and talk to us one of these days.'

Webland says: 'Do you know my name?'

He smiles and nods.

'How did you know it?'

The only answer is a wink and the mention of a little bird.

At the Naffy, on the other hand, in presenting his coupons the week before, he had been given only half the usual ration. When he drew attention to the fact that he'd always had double that amount, the girl snapped angrily: 'You never 'ave.' All the men complain of the attention and the manners at the Naffy.

An N.C.O. comes in one evening looking for spare beds. He spies Adam's, obviously unoccupied, and leaves sharply saying it may be needed, but whether for taking away or for occupation by some alien room-mate he doesn't hint. Incidents like this are bad for the nerves. Possible consequences of rumoured changes can utterly destroy one's peace of mind.

That was a bad day, for at breakfast, balancing a full plate of porridge on top of a full mug of tea and carrying another full plate in the other hand through a crowded canteen, over went the porridge on to Webland's tunic and the enamel plate clanged to the floor. Something of the sort was bound to happen sooner or later. Luckily there was no trouble over a replacement from the good-tempered cook, the same one who sometimes gives a forbidden second helping, saying: 'Not a word mind, quick. Remember you 'aven't 'ad it.'

At the radio room there seems even less work than usual. Thoughts of Christmas are at the front of everyone's mind. Not that the spirit and discipline there have ever been commendable. For instance, the permanent staff all smoke constantly in front of large red notices reading SMOKING STRICTLY PROHIBITED, officers doing the same when they occasionally pop in. One afternoon Webland read the newspaper, did the crossword puzzle and carried a small wooden box five yards to help someone; and that was more than some had accomplished. The staff are mostly engaged all day in carving model aeroplanes.

The two young L.A.C.s of the workshop are said to make money on the side by assembling home wireless sets out of the ample stores they live among. An elderly airman, who had served in the first war in the Royal Naval Air Service and afterwards owned an inn in the Isle of Man, has no high opinion of the young N.C.O.s for whom he has to make cups of tea when called for, and then wash up. He is on the permanent staff and does nothing else all day. He can't think why he isn't clerking or working a lathe, which he is good at. But he is too good-natured to be sour and too straight to become corrupted. How did Dr Johnson know that a soldier's time is passed in distress and danger or in idleness and corruption?

Two days before Webland's leave begins, Adam's leave expires. Webland works to get the room clean for his arrival, the fire burning and his unstolen bed made up in perfect kit inspection style. Then off, with the happy Welsh contingent, to London and the West for blessed Christmas.

What a contrast have been these second six weeks with those initial ones at Cadstone! There, all was cut and dried; good bullshit, progressive and inspiring; and the seaside weather had been superb. Here all is slack and soggy; bullshit bad and scarce, stagnant and dispiriting; and the fenland weather has been foul. A new and haunting figure, too, has crept upon the scene: that of the forgotten man. Without searching, Webland has himself talked with several; most of them are would-be pilots who made the mistake of falling sick in mid-course. Thank goodness that particular sword can never fall on him, nor is their sad problem his to solve. But what are their officers doing for them? Or have they none? Are these ghost-men off the record, non-existent?

If it weren't that his commission was about to come through Webland would be worrying about a detail in his own career. He has observed that every man who has come to the radio room from Cadstone and Cumberland is marked as R.O.u/t: Radio Operator, untrained. Hitherto Webland has been R.T.O.u/t: Radio Telephone Operator. What the difference is neither he nor his friends know but it must be specific. At present it doesn't seem worth while trying to stir up any inquiries. Observation and experience have made him cautious. The consequences are unpredictable and might be calamitous. So he resolves to merge himself with his R.O. friends and hope that his different calling won't be noticed. No doubt things will start moving when he returns from leave after Christmas; and anyway, R.O. or R.T.O., it's no more than a theoretical question, since Ops B is his destination and old Frank is waiting for him in readiness at dawn.

6

Mismustered

Take the tone of the company you are in.
LORD CHESTERFIELD – *Letters*

Christmas is over; leave is over. Webland sets off on the familiar one-man march back from the railway station to the camp. A business man he had talked to in the train from London rolls past him out of the station yard in his car, but Webland cares not at all, for the combination of frost, moonlight and boots works its magic on body and mind; and he is in no hurry.

'Welcome, Mr Webland. Did you have a good time?' says the S.P. at the camp gates; which is gratifying indeed from an unknown Redcap.

Adam is in, with a good fire and a hilarious account of Christmas military festivities. Weeks before this time he had been marked as a musician useful to the officers in what he describes as their sumptuous quarters, and so he was seconded to play his violin in the camp pantomime, *Cinderella*, with the two ugly Sergeants. He says it was really quite well done.

He tells also of the muddle of well-meant feeding on Christmas Day: quantities of ill-cooked food, tepid or cold, not enough plum pudding for everyone, hearty officers waiting on the men at the tables, beer full of whirling sediment, and many other incompetencies. Some seem to have enjoyed themselves, but not Adam, who is something of a gourmet.

He says that the L.A.C.s and the Flight Sergeant at the radio room had remarked that they missed Webland, who was always so cheerful and obliging and dependable. 'God forgive us, Adam; I thought we were nothing but a couple of scroungers these days like everybody else.'

After the journey and the emotions he feels an over-mastering desire for strong drink, when and where none can be got. Seldom has he felt the need so urgently. There is a small parcel on his bed bearing his home town's post mark. Inside is a letter from the village schoolmaster about a fund 'to send gifts to local men serving with H.M. Forces, and we hope you will accept the enclosure with best wishes from your friends at Amberdine . . .' The enclosure is nothing less than a bottle of whisky.

'A miracle, Adam, a miracle! Get your mug, quick!'

In the morning, after breakfast, the newsvendor outside the canteen greets him with friendly irony: 'Nice to be back, ain't it?' The first hard hours of return to servitude have produced no incivility and more than one agreeable sign of warm regard.

The morning's work is conveying two pieces of paper over to the Orderly Room. Webland mistakes the door, behind which works a Wing-Commander Spankington-Fobsclutch, A.F.C., handsome and elderly. His post-Noël greeting to Webland is: 'What the bloody hell do *you* want?' This might have given Adam a week's depression, but Webland is becoming crustacean and thinks to present the old crabstick with a framed New Year gift of some lines from *The Faerie Queene*:

'He was to weet a man of full ripe years
That in his youth had been of mickle might
But now weak age had dimmed his candle light
Yet was he courteous still to every wight.'

In the afternoon Webland is set to helping a man called Scrough to fill accumulators with acid. Scrough is one of the men in the married quarters whom he has let himself in for waking up in the morning because they have no watches. Webland also rouses the man in the next room to his and Adam's kitchen. He has to do this, for if he doesn't the man roars through the fireplace at any time from three o'clock onward to ask what time it is.

His social life is expanding as it never did in Civvy Street. He has been invited by the north countrymen in the house opposite to share their splendid food this New Year's Eve. He likes them very much, but feels more at home with the Welsh lot, whose conversation keeps him gorged with laughter and affection. If he should ever oversleep, which would astonish all the neighbours, not to mention the cook-house where he is always punctual, his friend the newspaper-man has promised to keep back his newspaper for him until at least a quarter to eight.

The evening he spends alone because Adam, now well in with the musicians, has contracted to play in a small orchestra at the Officers' Mess: a job he likes, if only for the good supper he is supplied with afterwards. The officers live, he says, most comfortably and make requests for more and more swing music. Webland has plenty to do occupying himself with domestic tasks, as well as going out to the Naffy to collect his weekly couponful of chocolate and buying cakes to eat later in the evening.

So the first day back swings him smoothly into the old routine, which he has reason to suppose will not go on much longer; for a man he knows, who has just passed his final interview for a commission and was about to be posted for training as a mechanic, has had the posting cancelled in view of his impending promotion.

New Year's Eve is not spent after all with the north-country party, for two appeals have come through for Webland's help, which, in his growing officiousness, he cannot forbear to reject. First, Davis's and Griffiths's fire has defeated them and Webland jumps at the chance of demonstrating the Adam method. He makes a flaming success of it. Then a flight mechanic in the next room calls in to ask: 'How do you report sick at this place?'

'Oh, you always have to be sick at 8 in the morning.'

'But how do you do it after duty?'

Neither of them knows. The chap's finger, and a very dirty mechanical one it is too, has begun to swell; so Webland who has been to many an A.R.P. lecture on first-aid without learning very much about it, treats the damaged finger with boracic and plaster and a show of confident efficiency.

Adam and he have had a serious discussion on Adam's future. It is absurd for him to knock about navvying, or even in some electrical trade, when he is such an accomplished violinist. Webland persuades him that it is his duty to re-muster as soon as possible as a bandsman and wear what he would call a wee golden lyre on the sleeve of his tunic. Since his leave he has brought his violin to the billet, and, with the mute upon it, he delights Webland at bed-time with soft playing of reels and strathspeys. Yes, patriot as he is, he must forget about fighting the enemy with anything but his bow and fiddle. He says that, for some reason not understood, they wouldn't let him be a bandsman when he was called up; he had to be a Radio Operator.

Yesterday they had said good-bye to Joyner, the elderly airman from the R.N.A.S., who so much disliked making cups of tea for the youths in the radio room. He is posted to a course at Cranwell, which sounds like something more suited to his experience and ability. Almost damp-eyed he shook hands and hoped Webland would visit him after the war in his public house. Adam promised that they would call in with their schooner from the Royal Yacht Squadron with Webland at the helm.

This rare piece of posting sense in Joyner's case stands out in contrast with the occupation of a small airman who passes by the camp football field soon afterwards. The man is moodily picking up lumps of mud to make the ground level for the players at three o'clock. He thinks it a strange way of helping to win the war. Webland cheers him by describing some of his own daily contributions. They recognize one another as sometimes sharing the same bench at breakfast, and agree that the times are well out of joint.

More human driftwood bumps into Webland next morning coming away from breakfast in the dark. This one is a comparative newcomer who went on leave early in December and didn't return. His mates missed him and supposed that he must be ill. He tells Webland that he has just left the R.A.F. hospital near his home, where he had had influenza and bronchitis, and that he is still unwell but was released yesterday. On getting back to camp at three o'clock this morning he went to his room in a house opposite Webland's to find it occupied by strangers, so he had to find himself a bed in a barrack block elsewhere.

Up at the radio room that afternoon the young Sergeant Air Gunner in charge of fresh trained radio lads has decided to get a blackboard and chalks and go through some electrical diagrams for their benefit. Webland and Adam think that here is a chance to pick up some knowledge, and they learn a little by joining in and asking such basic questions as: 'What exactly is a current?' and 'How does an accumulator work?' This seems so promising an occupation that the young Sergeant is prevailed upon to continue with his chalks on later occasions. He is by no means master of his subject, but there is much that he can teach duffers. They only hope his teaching is correct. Adam doubts it.

Other studies that Webland has discovered for himself are learning to identify aircraft from a book he has borrowed, and how to tap out words on a small buzzer in the Morse Code, for the better remembering of which he has devised an alphabetical mnemonic. After two months of sitting and standing and reading and trying not to listen to dance music and song and occasionally doing a manual job or running an errand, he feels that he is beginning to decay.

He is fit in body though, and is determined not to take to slouching with hanging head and rounded shoulders.

The other day, in fact, as he was walking briskly through the camp an airman whom he knew whistled to him from behind. On coming up the airman said: 'I thought it was you by your walk.'

Webland said: 'I hope it's a decent walk.'

'Oh, yes: a nice kind of swagger in it. Were you ever in the Army? Your moustache looks like as if you were.'

Good, thinks Webland; not slipping yet. But he had never suspected himself of possessing a military gait.

The cook plays a notable part in one's satisfaction with the cook-house food in the matter of extras. As he stands at the hatch doling out, he is in command and occasionally palms a prize across to his favourites. Webland doesn't know any of these cooks personally and is therefore astonished when at tea one day the server hides a great pat of margarine between his two chunks of bread with a conspiratorial look of friendliness. The Welsh lot do even better with smuggled rashers of bacon when there is a compatriot cook on duty.

Sometimes there is a treat for all. At breakfast one day a unique spectacle met the queue of airmen: a battery of a hundred or so fried eggs in a pan on the counter. With bacon and near coffee this was a breakfast to remember in the long desert of baked beans, potatoes, and other substitutes. Adam, arriving a quarter of an hour afterwards, joined Webland at his bench with a blind, yolkless egg, fried stiff as though starched, which, he said, the serving cook selected specially for him out of the middle of dozens of golden ones.

The first piece of morning routine after dusting the Flight Sergeant's desk, shaking the mats, and sweeping round the legs of lounging youths – being trained mechanics they don't do manual labour – is to find a perch on one of the hot radiator pipes in the radio room and wait for the mail. This is brought by a slow lad chosen for the job by the Flight Sergeant. He is one of many who has been grounded from training for air-crew because of having, as he says, no 'air-sense', which Adam thinks really means 'no bloody sense at all'. Since he has signalized his first morning as postman by going off to get his hair cut instead of making for the post office, it looks as though there is something in Adam's interpretation. On little incidents like this the idle airmen's welfare hangs.

After he has washed up the mechanics' dirty tea-cups Webland is needed to take a piece of paper to one of the hangars across the road. He enjoys staring at the caged brutes with their screws and wings and guns, so tame here, so deadly in the sky. On the inside wall of one hangar is chalked a phrase in Greek, said to have been put there by a Czech or Polish airman long before. Webland studies it and hopes to win applause by a quick translation; but his knowledge is too slight and he has to admit that it seems to be something about doing one's best but he can't exactly say what.

It is now very cold and parts of the camp ground are crusted mud, laced with ice and powdered with snow. Although the warmth of the Signals building is acceptable it is still better to move about and have something useful to do, so Webland is glad when he obtains what looks like a regular job of fetching articles on the hand-cart from a store five hundred yards away in company with an agreeable young man from Lancashire, named Digby. This work uses up about two hours in the morning and half an hour in the afternoon. The rest of the time is spent as before, lounging in the Signals building.

The two L.A.C.s, Flush and Squitchfield, who spend so much time putting mysterious radio parts together, having been promoted Corporals, send Webland over to the main stores with a voucher to extract some Corporals' tapes for them to sew on their sleeves. The Sergeant takes a glance at the voucher and another at Webland and says:

'Why don't they come for 'em themselves? Well, they can't 'ave 'em, see?'

Webland finds himself answering with what he hopes is an idiomatic phrase: 'That suits me all right.'

The Sergeant, working up his temper, for he has just been made a Sergeant himself and has put in for a commission and been accepted, continues:

'So they sent *you* along 'ere, did they? And you've seen service before' – pointing at Webland's medal and indignant that he should be fagged around by those young mechanics.

Webland hastily mumbles that it's only a Coronation Medal.

'I know, I know,' he scowls. 'Well, you just go back and tell *Corporal* Flush and *Corporal* Squitchfield to come and fetch it themselves.'

On his return to the radio room with the message, an inconsiderable neutral in this battle of Titans, he is stimulated to hear the Corporals' opinion that what the Sergeant really needs is a punch on the nose, and relieved to know that nobody thinks that he himself needs one. These two Corporals have never treated him otherwise than civilly, have given him only trivial tasks to perform and have always addressed him without sarcasm as Mr Webland.

That evening Webland decides to take his first bath in camp. Hitherto he has cleaned himself at the cold sink in his billet and, weekly, in a bath at his friend's rooms in Carchester. The baths are in one of the blocks where most of the trained airmen sleep and wash. He has been advised to take with him a plug for the waste hole, a light bulb for the electric socket, a rag to wipe the bath with first, and a macintosh upon which to lay his discarded clothes on the muddy floor. With these, and a candle, matches, soap, sponge, towel and shaving things, he finds one of the two bathrooms unoccupied in the building a couple of hundred yards away.

He is evidently supposed to undress in the passage outside and hang his clothes on hooks; but the risk of theft seems too great, so he steps inside clothed and locks himself in. There is still enough daylight left to observe that, though the floor is filthy, the bath is not. It also has a plug and a rag. The water is hot, and he contrives to keep his clothes from getting wet, to bathe and shave and start drying himself before the dreaded rattle at the door warns him that he must get cracking. In his hurry, and to avoid muddying his feet on the floor while dressing, he steps naked into his socks and boots: a foolish sequence, because in putting on his drawers and trousers they become liberally smeared inside with the muck he has so diligently schemed to avoid.

Back at the billet, they eat some cake and cheese of their own, supplemented by chocolate biscuits brought over by a lonely airman opposite, and, since Adam feels disinclined to play his violin that evening, spend a pleasant evening comparing notes about their early working days before the war. Adam's only defect, so far as Webland is concerned, is his nervous loquacity, but Webland has by this time got his second wind in dealing with that, and Adam's unselfishness and wit and honesty ensure that the two of them never fall out in their strange and cramped companionship.

Every night Webland sleeps soundly until three in the morning, when he wakes, re-sleeps until five, again until six, and finally until twenty to seven, when he leaps up, unwillingly; for the bed holds no more warmth in the frosty air. Then he calls such neighbours as need to be called. Adam, accustomed in his musical profession to later nights and later mornings, sleeps on until Webland sets off to be first in the queue for breakfast.

An airman says this morning that no more commissions are to be recommended for Administrative and Special Duties. This seems to contradict Frank Mead's assertion that such officers are badly needed, and Frank being a Squadron Leader in Operations surely ought to know. But since Webland has already long since been recommended and apparently accepted, he doesn't suppose that this new order, if it's true, will affect him. He thinks it would be rather dismal for a man rising forty to continue as an A/C2 merely for lack of technical and trade qualifications as an engineer or butcher or tailor or accountant, and serve throughout the war as a labourer under Sergeants and Corporals very little older than his children.

The petrol coupon question has come up again. Not forgetting that sinister deal with the Warrant Officer in charge of such matters a few weeks back, Webland is bold enough to visit him once more to ask for coupons for his car to meet him at the station when he next goes home on a 48-hour leave pass. Whether the Warrant Officer recognizes him or not, he gives a curt refusal, flourishing a copy of King's Regulations and saying that there's no question of coupons being issued to anyone who doesn't keep a car in the camp. This doesn't tally with past knowledge, but he judges it wise to accept the rebuke without comment, supposing it to be the recoil he has long expected for having refused to compound with the juggle over the mileage at the previous interview.

Petrol seems to be a great provoker of trickery, for that same day when Adam and he are sent over to the fuel stores with a voucher for five gallons, the Corporal who doles out the petrol hands over four. When Adam observes that it's five that he has signed for, the Corporal says: 'Do you expect me to open another bloody tin to give you a gallon?' That is really what they do expect, but they are both diffident about bandying words with superiors and so they return with what they've got and leave the man to sort it out with his equals.

Another curious piece of responsibility takes place at the clothing stores. When an airman thinks that any part of his tunic is past further mending, he may go and put in a claim for a new one. Webland has twice split his jacket across the shoulder and Adam has cleverly stitched it for him; but now he thinks it's time for a new one. He shows the garment to the N.C.O. in charge of the stores, and is told it's not nearly worn enough. But he is also told by an airman in the vicinity that all he has to do is to give the thing a couple of good wrenches, tear it apart a bit more, and all will be well. This, he declared, is the normal practice; and it works.

Two of the noisiest of the three inhabitants of the next room have been posted. When Webland asks the small airman cook left behind if they have actually gone, he replies: 'Yes, thank Christ; and they don't 'arf make a bloody mess.' Webland realizes more thankfully than ever how lucky he is to have Adam as his room-mate. They used to hear these departed men's shouted conversation through the fireplace with one foul favourite adjective predominant and continuous. Clean peace now ensues.

Adam and Webland have done all the swearing that they needed in their youth. Adam says he likes to hear it very occasionally, in the distance, for the sake of auld lang syne; but their habit now is to exercise their wit at its expense.

At Church Parade last Sunday Webland had arrived on the parade ground, and, failing to spot his own Signals Unit in the throng of grey overcoats, was starting to walk towards the boys coming down from the Signals building, when the Flight Sergeant in charge of the parade spotted him as a potential church shirker. 'Hey! Where yer goin', son?' Webland explained to his honorary dad. 'Well, fall in there!' Among a jumble of airmen and sailors he fell in and marched with them, behind a band – oh, those frozen fingers – to the icy cold theatre hangar, acting church, where the muslin covered chaplain, unless he was wearing a sheepskin lined cassock must have been the coldest worshipper of them all. Bluely he chattered: 'I'll make my sermon short', and he did.

Corporal Flush at the radio room, who thinks Webland something of a card and likes to hear what he calls a fresh Webland crack, wanted him to repeat what he had told another man about that freezing Church Parade. So he obliged, and recounted how the Flight Sergeant had popped him in the alien group of air and sea men, and how, approaching the holy hangar on the march, he had heard so much of the old sexual word in four letters that

I   123

he thought it would be more pious when inside to transfer himself to a group that were contented with its male and milder counterpart in six. (Only, of course, in the telling he used the actual oaths.)

'It's quite right wot 'e says,' the Corporal commented, 'only you don't look at it that way; you get so used to it.'

Webland has been interested to notice that the very few airmen whom he has come across, of whatever age, from the so-called minor public schools have not distinguished themselves by their greater unselfishness, chivalry, cheerfulness or comradeship; if anything, rather the reverse. But he realizes that, with so few examples to study, it would be foolish to draw any broad conclusions as to types and tendencies. These self-centred beings would perhaps have acted in the same way whatever schooling they had had. But he remembers Corporal Todd's words to him on this type of recruit at Cadstone.

Sharing troubles is at the very heart of comradeship. Having learnt now after four months of fairly close acquaintance that Webland's lot is in essence no different from theirs, in some respects they acknowledge worse, the original sixteen from Cadstone are always welcoming whenever Webland calls during the last period of the evening. They ply him with their private hoard of delicacies, bring back to him presents of food or shag tobacco from their homes, and enjoy hearing his impressions of life, past and present.

Davis, who comes from the Welsh border and shares a room with Griffiths from Caernarvon, has a tale of misery to tell. At Cadstone the condition of his teeth had been judged ripe for treatment, and he had endured many and painful sessions having them drilled and stopped and saved. At Swanton the dentist, holding other views, has pulled the whole lot out. So he is in a sad case. One small compensation he has in the form of a piece of paper authorizing him, since he can no longer bite, to claim a second helping of pudding at the cook-house. This chit is useful for his friends as well. But it will be a very long time, he thinks, before his dentures find out where he is and, finding, fit him.

Webland calls on these two friends, who are among the unhappiest of all the Welsh lot, and spends a long evening in their room commiserating with them and discussing political, financial and social questions. At the end they vote it a most profitable and entertaining evening, and beg him to repeat the visit as soon as possible. He promises he'll tell them more about his encounters in civilian life.

Adam comes back at bed-time from playing in the Officers' Mess, full of hope about his re-mustering. The Officers and fellow-musicians seem so much impressed by his violin playing that he thinks they will be able to see that he can save his livelihood after the war. The musicians, he says, were surprised when he told them that he was sleeping in a room with Webland, who did his share of washing up the crockery and pulling the hand-cart. They couldn't understand why he should be doing such things instead of going direct into the Service as an Officer.

The agreeable Warrant Officer has been posted from the Signals branch and a Sergeant comes round the regular and irregular staff with a tin, collecting money to bid him good-bye with. Everyone is sure that this is permissible, but Webland withholds his subscription, explaining what the Police had told him at Coastington about all presents to N.C.O.s being against regulations. However, when an Officer appends his own name to the list, he supposes he had better relent; so he contributes sixpence, judging that to be a proper sum from an A/C 2.

Wouldn't it be wonderful, he thinks, if an Officer were to come among the forgotten airmen and say: 'Well, how are you getting on? I know how dreary it must be for you all waiting month after month like this. Is there anything I can do to ease things a bit?' But there is no contact with any Officer at all; except on a day when a young one passed through the radio room, where Webland was sitting smoking and reading the newspaper, and said 'Good morning'. But he was newly arrived and probably shy. Webland rewarded him by standing up and removing his pipe from his mouth. And on another day in the cookhouse an Officer passed through calling: 'Any complaints?' Webland, having difficulty at the moment in separating his cabbage from the sand it was boiled with, thought Here's my chance, and looked round to answer; but by that time the Officer was gone.

By contrast here is David Jenkins one evening, having heard that Webland has no coal for his fire, trotting into his room with a large faggot of sticks he had secured for himself earlier in the day and laying them in the fireplace. Only those who know how priceless such little acquisitions of fuel are, to be hoarded by the finder and concealed from all others, can measure the unselfishness of men like Jenkins and the other friends.

The authorities are still generous with 48-hour passes. Most of the forgotten men are getting them every three or four weeks; and that does much to relieve their dissatisfaction. It also eases the strain of close quarters in the billets, for Adam will be away one time and Webland another, and both return refreshed and reinterested in each other's doings.

After two and a half months of Swanton almost the first small piece of bullshit is imposed upon the married quarters billets: a kit inspection; and, it may be supposed, high time too. It is arranged for immediately after breakfast, so Adam and Webland neatly lay out the thirty-odd articles of their service possessions along their beds: from spoon to macintosh, button stick to haversack. It is no surprise to them to wait alongside, like stall-holders at a parish bazaar, from eight until a quarter to twelve, when Sergeant Hole, the grounded air-gunner mislaid by Records, and Corporal Flush, make a cursory examination of their display. Webland will have to account for a service shaving-brush which he had never liked the look of and had purposely left behind at Cadstone; otherwise all is in order and has to be stuffed back again into the canvas kit-bag.

It seems likely to be an exceptionally hard winter. There has been slight snow or hard frost for a fortnight, and now the cisterns and pipes in the married quarters are all frozen. To find running water the occupants go across to one of the blocks a hundred yards away and there do what washing they must. It is well on such occasions, says Adam, to remember the thousands in the cities bombed out, hurt and killed, or the millions of homeless Europeans who would give all they possess to enjoy the conditions that are browning off the safe Swanton airmen.

The cook-house is always warm and at the exit there is in a dark closet a tap of ever running water in which the eaters rinse their greasy irons. Courtesy here is rare, and Webland's fails him at the pinch. One day when his turn at the tap arrives he is holding his irons in the gush from it when the man following impatiently pushes his irons forward and holds them just above Webland's. It is the work of an evil second for Webland to tilt the inside of his spoon to take the force of the jet, so that the scalding water bounces off on to the rude airman's fingers. Adam is two places behind in the queue, and when he rinses his irons the man following him tries to get his own under the tap at the same time, knocking Adam's knife into the sink. Adam says quietly: 'You've knocked my knife in. Will you pick it out?' The man dips his hand in and pulls it back again sharply, crying: 'Christ! It's too hot', and vanishes.

The very next day, what Jenkins calls the great God Thaw comes in at the gallop. Snow turns to ice needles, ice needles to cold strings of rain, getting less and less cold as the day wears on, and by evening the waters at the billet are loosed from the solid pipes; but not through the taps. Adam and Webland are sitting by the fire darning when a stampede and a shouting arise from the room upstairs where live two airmen cooks. Since these cooks occasionally go wild up there and yell curses at the house next door for banging or singing too loud, Webland pays no heed, though Adam pricks up his musical ears and looks apprehensive. Then down the wall farthest from the beds comes a deluge in the form of twelve streams of rushing water, and through the door burst two wild little cooks, crying: 'Where the 'ell's the tap to turn it off at the main?' It is found under the sink by Webland's bed: a nut with no key; but with a scrap of iron it is manipulated and the torrent checked. It only remains to broom the water out of the room and make plans for a further waterless week.

The advantage of their use of the kitchen for sleeping quarters has been chiefly the lock and the key as a preventive of pilfering while they are away. But this last day of January, their almost three months run of security has come to an end, and in a fashion that has shaken Adam's none-too-steady nerves to their roots.

When Webland returns from the day's lounging and lugging he finds Adam in despair. He tells Webland that shortly after one o'clock, when he was getting ready for his afternoon off in Carchester, the Station Warrant Officer, a high functionary of the camp, had paid a surprise visit to the married quarters. His wish, it seems, was to move Adam and Webland into what he considered a more suitable room next door. It may be mentioned that they always keep their room clean and tidy. But, Adam says, this is how the Warrant Officer proceeded. The words in brackets stand for the paramount service oath.

Throwing open the door of the room he stood at the entrance surveying Adam, the sink, the beds and the two grinning plumbers who were repairing the taps, with a glare of consummate disgust. The rest of the act was in the shape of a monologue from the Warrant Officer, opening with the not-to-be-answered question: 'What the (sexual) hell's this?' Talk of that quality sears Adam's soul, and when the answer shot from the questioner: 'A (sexual) pigsty', with a blizzard of similar animadversions on the habits of airmen who dwell in such conditions, coupled with the promise that he'd 'have every (sexual) key taken away', Adam, mindful of his precious bow and violin, was in a state little short of collapse.

Webland does his best to soothe poor Adam. He assures him that this sort of behaviour by a Warrant Officer is merely a cover for a lack of basic confidence, and as such is too contemptible to be hurt by; also that they will probably find themselves more comfortable in the next room although it is a public way through for all the dirty-footed occupants of the house of whom there are only four at present; and that they can easily find a key to fit the lock on the cupboard there in which they can store their things safely. But he is indignant that a middle-aged musician, some high way up in his profession, should have been subjected to a foul and unmerited tirade from an apparently responsible Officer.

One happy result of the inspection is that a new and larger delivery of coal has been made, although it is generally supposed to be not so much for the benefit of the human beings as of the tanks and pipes which are once more starting to freeze up at the return of the north-east wind.

After a night in the new bedroom, upon which between four and five hours' work has been done by them, Adam and Webland realize that the change has been for the better, and they set out to prepare for another bout of station manoeuvres in fairly good heart.

While digging two thin holes for aerials with his pick-axe and spade Webland makes the acquaintance of a soldier of twelve years' service, including Dunkirk. The soldier had removed an immense bucket of urine from close proximity to the hut beside which he was excavating, for which he was very grateful. Webland learns from him that he is from Birmingham and that his wife has left him for another fellow while he has been serving. This, added to the fact that the soldier keeps calling him 'Sir', serves to produce in Webland complicated emotions. What can he say?

Putting up the aerial pole later, in the presence of the

young mislaid air-gunner Sergeant, Webland breaks unusually into song. He sings a popular tune he has picked up from the ubiquitous B.B.C., called something like *Rosa Lay*. 'That's a rather low-brow one for you, Webland, isn't it?' says the Sergeant. Suppressing the answer, 'Low-brow songs for low-brow work', he gives the Sergeant a wink, signifying that he is not really as high-brow as they might think him. Someone told him not long ago that Sir Stafford Cripps had complained of suffering from intellectual starvation when he was in Russia. That must be really high-brow; among all those chess players too. No; that's not the kind of starvation that Webland suffers from here, if indeed he is starved at all.

So far as he is concerned Swanton is entirely a man's world. He has not tried to gain the affections of any of the pert girls behind the counter at the Naffy, but he is very sure that his face and manner leave them cold, if not frozen. And for the WAAFs' dance last night in some hut, to which each girl invites an airman, no invitation reached Webland. In any case he doesn't feel he could have done full justice to one.

Snow has been falling in these first days of February, and all hands, including Webland's, have been busy shovelling clear ways on camp and airfield for men and machines. This is not suitable work for Adam but he tackles it with the rest, and then goes to see if his Roman Catholic padre can help him over his obstructed re-mustering. The padre is not encouraging and seems more interested in the religion of Adam's room-mate and his parentage. 'Oh, that's Montagu Webland's son, isn't it?' All the officers seem to have heard of Webland, but none of them ever comes to talk to him as Squadron Leader Hooper had done at Cadstone.

In the new bedroom the fire has dampers which operate out or in according to whether the bath water and the kitchen oven behind are to be heated or merely the room and the chimney. This evening socks and stockings and towels are put in the oven to dry and the damper pulled out and forgotten. When an hour or so have passed the kitchen becomes filled with smoke and on the oven door being opened all the articles inside are aglow and past saving. Adam and Webland are so much depressed by this that they move across to the Naffy and treat themselves to a dish of Cornish pasty with coffee, costing tenpence for the two. This is a rare treat and they feel as though they are at Claridges. Music is provided, too, by a very dirty-looking soldier at the piano, who puts in more work with his feet than he docs with his oil-stained fingers.

Another thaw turns the snowy camp into a mess of pools and marzipan, but a quick succeeding frost out of a scything north-east wind soon sets the ground back into iron and glass at every slope and angle. The coal has all been burnt. 'We shall have to steal again,' says Adam; and they know the ways of doing it.

Up at the radio room the life goes demoralizingly on. Webland determines to remain punctual and willing, concentrating on what few jobs he does. After breakfast and lunch, although they are all his superiors, the young radio chaps now bring him sweet and milky cups of tea which they brew in the adjacent workshop. Unsolicited as they are he finds these ministrations most cheering. The boys are gay to watch; their language and spirits are terrific. They come for help with Shakespeare quotations and witty words in the crossword puzzles and laugh when he gives a prompt solution.

Re-mustering seems to be in the air. Adam is still groping up various channels. He and Webland have composed a grovelling letter to 'higher authority', stating his case to be a musician and beginning and ending 'Sir, I have the honour ...' as though he were an indignant golfer. But more important to Webland is an announcement that all Radio Operators (his mates) and Radio Telephone Operators (himself alone) are strongly advised by the Air Ministry to re-muster into other trades, as there will be a considerable wait before training for these two trades can commence.

This follows quite neatly on what the Squadron Leader here told Adam the other day: that there was such a desperate need for Radio Operators that he would be most unlikely to be released from that trade in order to become a musician. And this is why the airmen are becoming inured to shocks and changes and advice, and why most of them resolve not to budge. Webland says: 'I bet you in another month they'll stick up a notice howling for everyone to re-muster as Radio Operators.' Anyway it won't affect him, now comfortably resigned to waiting at Swanton for his commission, if need be until midsummer.

It is getting time for another 48-hour pass. The pass is duly issued and he goes home again. Returning to Swanton in the train from London he finds himself in a compartment with three commuting business men a very few years older than himself. He always enjoys listening to their opinions on politics, patriotism and anything other than business, and usually finds that that is what they prefer to talk about.

One of them is raging against the futile defence of Singapore, declaring that if he could have his way he'd have all the old school ties shot, for the whole thing is obviously their fault. To this a slightly older man replies that the rager knows nothing about it: 'You don't know any more than I do.' The rager then reckons that it would be a jolly good thing to get rid of Churchill and put Lord Beaverbrook in his place, which makes the older man laugh so much that he can make no reply.

With these weighty matters to occupy his mind Webland soon covers the two mile walk from the railway station to the camp to find Adam in a fuss about an inspection of rooms tomorrow by the C.O. and the M.O. Not being privy to their likes and dislikes Webland doesn't know how to arrange the room for their approval and decides to leave it as it is; but Adam isn't satisfied. Webland relents so far as to lock up their honey and cake in the cupboard in case the inspectors should take a fancy to them. He supposes they are unlikely to make off with his *Browning* or his *Golden Treasury*.

Another bout of manoeuvres takes place in tolerable weather with Adam and Webland by this time veritably expert Receiving-You-Loud-and-Clearers. The only variant for Webland is a more exhausting piece of exercise for him than he had expected. Presenting himself at the start wearing his anti-everything costume, after having laboriously waddled three-quarters of a mile to his underground post, he is almost immediately selected by a Sergeant to accompany him to a spot a mile and a half up a ploughed field hill, where he had already spent some of the afternoon, to find out why they could get no response from those manning it. Having fixed them up – and a heavy walk it was in his massive garb – and returned to the dug-out, an Officer wishes to be guided to the spot on the hill they have just come from. So Webland escorts him, floundering about through mud and barbed wire in the moonless night for another hour or so. He is so tired at the end of it that he feels he really has achieved something to help the war, even if it is only his own exhaustion. The rest of the manoeuvres pass as usual in rest and conversation, direct or radiophonic.

Back at the old radio room, the personnel of which shrinks and grows as airmen leave and arrive, there is always plenty of lively talk. Criticism of the Government over the loss of Singapore and the escape of the German warships in the English Channel is as copious and unimaginative as any man in the train could desire. Constitutionally Webland, for all his independence of outlook, is inclined to be pro-Government whatever its complexion, and this causes him to put a favourable construction on most of their actions.

But lighter moments normally prevail. Mills, a merry, intelligent young artisan, who is reading a technical book beside Webland, his chair tilted back and his feet up, mumbles: 'This is all balls, this book.' Webland, writing a letter and not looking up, dreamily replies: 'Yes, I should

say that balls is a very just description of that book';
which pleases Mills greatly and causes him to declare that
he and Webland agree on most subjects.

So the wasteful days pass at Swanton Signals Section,
while half the world fights for its life and a good percentage dies. The frost returns once more.

On a lorry, hitch-hiking, Webland meets a Sergeant
whom he knows and who was passed for a commission
by the Air Ministry a day after Webland. This Sergeant
says that he has just heard from someone in the Ministry
that there is a long hold up of non-technical commissions,
administrative and so on, and that it will not be let down
for six or seven months. Therefore it seems that it will
be August or September before Webland leaves Swanton.
He'd as soon stay where he is as anywhere, since he
doesn't suppose he could get released to take up a job in
industry during the period of waiting; but it is amusing
to observe himself gradually coming to accept just such
a position as he has deplored in so many others. Still,
most of the people at Swanton are decent. That is not to
be undervalued; and he would miss the companionship
of Adam and his Welsh friends.

Pay day is always interesting, for Webland never knows
how much cash he is going to be given. Usually it has
been a pound; once it was something over three. This
time they have given him a guinea. As he is passing along
the building studying his extra shilling a Corporal makes
him put it in a collecting bag he is holding. Webland asks
if he has to do this and is told 'Yes'. He hears afterwards
that it is a voluntary subscription for sports, but who
receives how much of the money collected is unknown.
The collection is naturally resented by men who are old,
educated and experienced enough to care how money is
raised and administered, and such mysterious goings-on
tend to breed something that does not make for the much
desired *esprit de corps*.

In the meantime he is able now and then to add to the
non-electrical learning of the N.C.O.s of the Signals

Section. Reading from the *Daily Mirror* one morning
the young air-gunner Sergeant looks up and says: 'Wot's
a lesbian, Flight?' The Flight Sergeant knows, but all the
same appeals for confirmation to Webland. 'Sexual per-
version – ain't it, Webland?'

'Yes, Flight, but only women with women'; and he
explains the derivation of the word.

Instead of going home on his next 48-hour pass at the
end of February Webland spends it with his wife in
London. There, in his aircraftman's uniform he has a meal
with an older friend, Cuthbert Latimer, who works at the
summit of the nation's affairs, and is shocked to hear that
Webland has been six months in the ranks without progress or promotion, still untrained and waiting for a long-
promised commission. He says that something had better
be done to speed things up. Webland says: 'Don't do
anything. If you interfere you'll ruin the whole object of
my design, which is to see how soon I can get on in the
new system. It may not be working properly, but I am
determined to give it a thorough trial. It must come right
soon, because I've done everything required better than
most; and I'm having a wonderful experience.'

On the morning after Webland's return to camp, David
Jenkins shows him a prominent article in one of the
popular picture papers, attacking Montagu Webland as
a selfish old man who is hindering the war effort by
attempting to enrich himself at the country's expense.
Jenkins says he has heard some airmen discussing it in
the cook-house and suggesting that it might give Webland cause for a libel action. He himself is full of indig-
nation; and so, when they hear of it, are all the other lads.

This newspaper attack, although more direct and savage
than many past ones at the same target, does not affect
Webland's emotions so much as does the knowledge that
not one of his acquaintances at Swanton seems to believe
that there could be a word of truth in such a charge. So
far from being cast down by the incident he feels uplifted
by its consequences.

Pondering this matter of loyalty as he walks away from the cook-house, he absent-mindedly and very smartly salutes a Warrant Officer. Warrant Officers, as he knows very well, are not salutable; and Warrant Officers as often as not are tigers in correction. But this one is a cheery, ruddy, tubby Warrant Officer who is neither angry nor surprised at Webland's complimentary misdemeanour. Instead of snarling: 'I'm not a bloody Officer, you know', he smiles and says: 'I'm only a W.O.'

'Sorry, sir,' says Webland, 'I wasn't thinking.'

The W.O. remarks that the weather keeps cold; and so they part, on Webland's side with the thought that perhaps it might be better to be a Warrant than a Commissioned Officer after all. He need never bother about not being saluted; and if he is saluted in error he will know exactly what to say: 'I'm *only* a W.O.'

The first commission of anyone whom Webland knows personally has just come through: that of an L.A.C. in Signals who had his interview a month after Webland and is to be posted to Uxbridge for training. He tells Webland that most people say it is absolutely essential to pull what strings you can if your commission is to materialize with any speed. He does not say how many strings have been pulled for himself; nor does Webland tell him that he has just cut his own most powerful string.

The first week in March brings the first rain for about two months, and spring is moving. So is the Air Ministry. The morning excitement among the lads is that, having been at Swanton for four months and recently advised to re-muster away from being Radio Operators, two of them have been posted for training as such. They had of course declined to re-muster. It is the first time any of them has had a move and there is much wild speculation.

Adam, too, hears that he is to be examined as to his musical ability. In order, he says, to save the nation the expense of his making a special trip to Uxbridge for the purpose, he is to be tested here by an L.A.C. who has decidedly less experience and proficiency than himself.

This good, or fairly good, news gives them both strength to face the lunch of splintered bones in gravy and jam in concrete tart with metallic tasting custard. Nor do they mind the now pelting rain. But that evening, brought on by the spring change, or the unnatural meal, or even by the general sense of movement in the once stagnant ranks, gastric influenza, or so they diagnose it, strikes them both down. They will both, however, drop in their tracks before reporting sick, so they totter to an early bed where Webland reads his companion into a rapid sleep on Browning's poetry.

Perhaps their diagnosis was too precipitate, because the morning finds them practically recovered. Gastric it surely was, but influenza certainly not. Adam, anyway, is well enough to go into Carchester in the afternoon to lead the second violins in a rehearsal at the Guildhall.

Digby, Webland's frequent companion in pulling the hand-cart, has returned from his 48-hours at Lancaster. There he has told a Communist friend about Webland, and this friend has warned him seriously against getting corrupted by the aristocracy; but, Digby says, the man is only against aristocrats because he'd so much like to be one himself; a common state of mind in men of a certain temperament. Perhaps Digby is right.

Just as he is leaving for Carchester to watch Adam lead his second violins, one of their friends shouts across to Webland: 'You're posted for training as a Radio Operator with Davis and Skelding.' This doesn't suit Webland at all, but he refuses to let the news interfere with their evening arrangements.

The concert is good and the conductor tells Webland afterwards that Adam's presence among the fiddles was invaluable and that he was better than the professional leader of the orchestra. So back to Swanton and to bed, to find out more about this business of being posted in the morning.

It appears that the posting is only a rumour, though the airmen's jungle telegraphy is often right in such

matters. It is the general opinion that even if Webland
is posted, the posting will be cancelled because of his
commission. However, he realizes that he must be prepared for any folly.

A reference to the malicious newspaper article of a few
days ago is made by a small rough airman whom he has
never known well. He comes militantly up to Webland
and says:

'I've got something for you to write to the (sexual)
papers about, Mr Webland, to 'elp yer dad. Well, you
just go in the Blocks and look at all the (sexual) waste
of material goin' on in there. Why don't they (sexual)
well put that right?'

Back in three days' time from another 48-hours at
home, Webland finds that he has indeed been posted.
Is this the moment to raise a loud query with the Orderly
Room about his ambiguous designation? Such action
would either prove futile or result in separation from his
friends. There is nothing to be done but obey orders,
set off round the camp collecting signatures on his
Clearance Chit, bid farewell to as many of his pals as he
can find, and go.

All next day Webland, Davis and Skelding spend
together unwinding themselves, as it were, from the
strings that have held them at Swanton, visiting every
branch of the camp to procure signatures to a statement
that they leave clear of crimes and impediments. Webland
has been placed in charge of the travelling trio and is
responsible for the arrival of them all at the new place of
training, which is a camp called Bindover in the West
Country.

At the signing of his Clearance Chit the Adjutant asks
him some questions about his future. They have never
conversed before. Webland tells him that he has been
posted to a Radio Operators' course, whereas he has been
listed throughout his R.A.F. career as a future Radio
Telephone Operator; that he has discovered that he is
now over the age limit for both courses; and that he has

been expecting to be commissioned for the past five months. The Adjutant says he knows about the commission, because the Air Ministry have been inquiring about him two or three days ago. He asks if his papers are up at Blackpool. Webland says he's never been to Blackpool. Adjutant says: 'Where were you interviewed?'

Webland says: 'Cadstone, Coastington and Air Ministry, London, sir.'

Adjutant says: 'Have they got your papers?'

Webland, not understanding the exact nature of these papers, says:

'I don't know, sir.'

Adjutant says: 'Well, we haven't got them here.'

If that can be called a ray of light, it has been shed on the darkness encircling his commission. Perhaps these unknown papers have been lost. He has heard of such happenings.

Having warned the cook-house the night before that they will all need breakfast at six-thirty next morning, and rations as well, the three travellers set off at seven for the Guard Room with kit-bags and one piece of paper to serve as a pass for them all, from the Guard Room to the lorry, to the railway station and so to London. At Paddington they decide to separate and meet again there in time for the one-fifteen for Bindover.

During the three hours of separation Webland, who has the piece of paper in his pocket, is stopped by a Redcap. Reading that there should be three airmen instead of one, he asks some searching questions which Webland manages to answer satisfactorily. The Redcap is in two minds about arresting him for not being three airmen, but finally says: 'O.K. But you go and find them quick. For Christ's sake don't lose them or you'll be on a two-five-two. You know wot that is, don't yer?' Webland says he does.

Only slightly conscious of the crime of having left Davis and Skelding safely at the station instead of bringing them with him to see his sister, Webland returns to

Paddington, anxious lest they really have made a dash for freedom and left him to face the music of this two-five-two.

But they are on the platform; the train is caught; and by five o'clock that evening they are at Bindover in the dusk, telephoning to their new abode for transport.

7
Sparks

Gremio: O this learning, what a thing it is!
SHAKESPEARE – *The Taming of the Shrew*

By this time an expert at waiting for orders, Webland finds the two and a half hours outside the railway station pass soon enough. A lorry then conveys the three Swantonians and a dozen or so other airmen to the camp about five miles away, where they clatter to the ground to be sorted into threes and marched to the long wooden building allotted to them. Into hut M33, blacked out and dimly lighted, each man staggers with his pack and baggage in search of an empty bed.

The best place that Webland can find among the thirty is one somewhere near the middle of the room, but soon an airman who has been in residence for some weeks directs him to a better one by the far wall, with a large wooden box beneath the bed. Fitted with a padlock, here is a storage place safe from pilferers.

After six months in uniform this is Webland's first real experience of barrack-room life. Wondering how to wash, his memory darts back thirty years to the private school dormitory. There a line of loose basins had stood. He couldn't remember where the water to fill them had come from in those days before the 1914 war; certainly not through taps. Perhaps maids had carried jugs for them morning and evening.

Here he soon discovers that washing is done in a large,

wet room along a stony passage and its name is 'Ablutions', or more simply 'Blooshuns'. As one of the newcomers says to Webland, the word is derived from the verb 'to bloot'. He is grateful for that early sally.

To the sound of radio music the shadowy airmen set about unpacking kit. At the long table in the centre of the hut the Corporal in charge starts to make himself heard above the din, asking for the names and numbers of the new men. When it comes to '107 Webland!' the Corporal pauses before dealing with the next man's name.

'Montagu,' he says reflectively. 'Any relation?'

'Yes, Corporal.'

'Ought to be shot.'

What an unexpected biff in the dusk. No previous men or N.C.O.s had suggested such a thing to him before, whatever they might have thought. Did the Corporal mean that Webland the son or Webland the father ought to be shot? The roll-call proceeds to its end and, after a visit to the cook-house, they all begin preparations for bed.

But there is a bit more good luck yet before the trying day is done. His bed neighbour, in the course of fraternization, reveals that he is a Roman Catholic.

'Hurray,' says Webland, 'then you won't mind my saying my prayers.'

This grave-looking man from the North Country, whose name is later discovered to be Paul, confesses that he always says his prayers in bed for fear of leg-pulls from unholy airmen. He is over nervous; for, beyond one or two interested glances, there can be observed no sign of a smirk whatever. In due course Webland gets inside his bed of five blankets and two sheets, not too dirty, though left over from the last unknown airman. A first night is always a strain, in camps as in theatres, and he hopes for rapid unconsciousness. Lights and radio are extinguished at 10.45.

Both come on together at 6.15 next morning, brightening sleepy airmen, the first action of some being to stretch out a blind hand for the bedside cigarette packet from which courage can be kindled to face the troubles of the day.

The first duties, as might be expected, are the filling in of forms and the very familiar physical examination at the M.I. Room. There poor Davis, who has already had to leave behind at Cadstone all his natural teeth as well as his two chief comrades, Griffiths and Thomas, is dealt by Fate another sickening blow. In deepest gloom, he announces afterwards with the ghost of a mirthless laugh, that he has been rejected for the course because of his eyesight, and that he is to be placed forthwith on what is officially called 'General Duties', commonly, of course, G.D., which means in this case sweeping up round the camp. Webland and Skelding comfort him as best they can, but the future looks ugly for him now.

In the morning light the Corporal, whose name is Bowman, takes stock of his new charges. He explains that he intends his hut to be the smartest in the block, adding the customary clause that if they'd play ball with him he'd play ball with them, otherwise – and then came the threats. 'Fair enough?' Fiercely he speaks and fiercely looks, but there is a spurious air about it and few are really intimidated. Soon afterwards he approaches Webland's bed and sits on it beside him. A wise Corporal to come to terms as soon as possible, since he and Webland are going to have to spend six weeks of nights not fifteen feet apart, and their introduction the evening before has been ill-omened.

Webland begins to think that he has seen Bowman's face before. Bowman, no doubt after searching his own memory, had sought information from the two Swantonians as to Webland's identity. He must have been vexed when he recalled that shortly before the war it had been himself, as a small functionary in the town near Webland's home, who had invited this very Webland to come to the town and make a public appeal on behalf of some national cause. Webland had not accepted the invitation, but he had met Mr Bowman once or twice in the town; and now Corporal Bowman and Aircraftman Webland were face to face again and, as it were, upside down.

Both now remember the pre-war meeting well, and both forbear to mention it. The re-meeting is already embarrassing enough. It is for Corporal Bowman to speak and he takes by no means the only and perhaps not quite the honest, but certainly a sensible line. It is a worse situation for him than for Webland. He says that he has only just realized who Webland is, that Webland mustn't take to heart what he had said, for it had only been meant as a joke. Webland, who feels no animosity, replies that he is old enough to understand these things and won't let the incident upset him. The Corporal then indicates that he will go out of his way to help him in any way he can; Webland thanks him, and the interview ends.

After the mess of Swanton the clean, hard bullshit of Bindover is not unwelcome. The hut has to be kept superlatively clean and the main area of attention is, as usual in the tramping life of the services, the floor. So with broom, polish, rag, and bumper – a weighted, felt-covered block, hinged to a five foot pole – that floor has to be groomed by the hour to satisfy the Corporal's natural wish to earn the praise of the Flight Sergeant and, if he should come round inspecting, of the Officer. If there lacks any article that might serve to improve the shining hut, the Corporal will order the men to procure it; and not by delicate words and means. He works himself up on the subject until, by the time he reaches his peroration, he is almost screaming.

'I don't care how you geddid, but you godder geddid. Savvy?'

At first this method makes everyone rather edgy; they wonder if he may be insane; but it soon loses much of its impact, without however becoming totally ineffective. The hut shines, the men don't become sullen, and the Corporal keeps his voice and his sanity.

It was a Thursday when Webland and the new batch

had arrived for the Radio Operators' Training Course. By Saturday the military formalities have been completed and the initiation into their electronic teaching performed. At midday on Saturday comes Corporal Bowman's reward: honeyed words from the Officer.

Each airman stands beside his bed upon the bedspace, for the cleanliness of which he is peculiarly responsible, while the Officer enters. This morning he has come to show a WAAF officerette how a unit should be kept. The men hear him explain that this hut is the smartest in the Wing: no dark and dirty corners to be discovered anywhere: a model of its kind. Corporal Bowman and his airmen feel very proud. After five rotting months at Cadstone here is morale once more to lift the heart: morale, not based upon respect or affection for the N.C.O. – he is too excitable to be ranked with the Corporals and Sergeants at Cadstone – but none the less morale of a sort, and profitable. The sight of an Officer, too, is inspiring, if not to all, certainly to Webland.

The hours of radio training are arranged in shifts, day and night. This Saturday, for instance, the afternoon is free; work is resumed from 6 p.m. until midnight. Supper is served in the cook-house at 12.30 a.m. and the men creep to bed in the dim blue light without too much clatter so as not to wake up the half-dozen or so who are in a more advanced state of training and have gone to bed at a normal hour.

On Sunday, which is free, Webland stands in a queue for a cold half-hour after breakfast to hire a bicycle at 1/4d for the day. He is lucky enough to get the very last; a red one with a loose saddle and worn brakes. He had decided to visit a friend who lives about fifteen miles away, but having telephoned a warning from a camp call-box and found his friend had gone away, and heavy rain having started to fall, there is nothing for it but to leave the machine in the store-room of the hut until it is time to return it in the evening.

In the hut the radio set plays on. This box must be a

noisy cousin of the radio which all the training course is to be about: the same family name but not much else in common. The purpose of a Radio Operator, as Webland has by now discovered, is to operate an instrument known as a goniometer, an angle measurer. In a manner to be learnt, the instrument's task is to detect and show by an illuminated line on a glass fluorescent screen the mark of an aeroplane at any distance up to about forty miles and fix its position in the sky, at the same time indicating whether the aeroplane is friendly or hostile. The process is called Radio Direction Finding or R.D.F., and the distinguishing sign of hostility or otherwise is known as I.F.F., which means Identification Friend or Foe. More initials for Webland to memorize. He should have no difficulty, if he keeps his wits, in distinguishing I.F.F. from the medical term F.F.I., or Free From Infection.

The training is both practical and theoretical. As well as learning the delicate touch of the knobs on the gonio, the men have to be taught about the construction of the instrument, with its cathode ray tube, inside which electrons and protons and other infinitesimals are set to hurtle a millimetric distance to and fro at the speed of light; all illustrated in words and diagrams by a young Corporal Instructor to a class of airmen at their desks with pencils and notebooks.

Never having troubled before to know how even the electric light worked, Webland is relieved to find that his brains are in good working order and that he should be able to understand no less than most of the others, and perhaps a bit more. Some of his class-mates are lads of twenty or under, and some are rather nearer Webland's own age; almost all seem keen to learn about this fascinating subject.

On returning from radio work to hut one morning Webland finds a copy of his county weekly newspaper on his bed. This is Corporal Bowman's proof that his soft words are not without substance.

Although the hut is always warm, when it rains, as it

146

does in quantity this month of March, there is no place to dry wet overcoats. Putting the spongy garment on again a few hours later Webland finds especially disagreeable. Another minor drawback in off duty hours is that the men are forbidden to lie on their beds in the daytime before 4 p.m., because sheets and blankets and biscuits have to be placed and remain in a rectilinear pile at the foot end of the springless bed.

The food, eaten at unusual hours, is now and then outlandish, and there is not quite so much of it as there had been at Swanton; but on the whole it seems to taste better. Perhaps that is because hard work begets good appetites. Tea at 6.45 p.m., for instance, is pickles and warm blocks of cheese, bread, margarine and jam. Again Webland thanks his stars and stomach that he has never had much more interior discrimination than a seagull.

He always enjoys getting a shine on his badge and buttons, but the boots he never can get into such condition as Corporal Cowley would have approved, and in consequence he takes no pleasure in their service; nor much in dusting and polishing his bed-space. He is still interested in darning, but not in sewing rents in trousers and jackets.

After class, the men are lined up for a quarter of an hour's P.T. Fortunately they are not issued with the singlet and rude linen shorts, as on the cliffs of Cadstone, but, discarding tunics, they are made to perform a few contortions and partner-wrestlings. The Instructor announces that the drill is not compulsory for those over thirty-five, but everyone joins in.

It is good to be properly regimented once more. Webland would have liked some parade-ground drill, with rifle and bayonet, and, of course, a band; but in the technical branches that could not be expected. The days and nights, though, are neatly carved into slabs for radio work, for hut work and for free time, and the rhythm brings peace of mind, which is a fair substitute for timeless freedom.

During that first week the Officer comes again to Hut M33 to inspect the kit of five men who have passed the course and are to leave at four o'clock next morning. He thanks the whole hutful for the way in which they keep the place and again says it is by far the cleanest and tidiest hut of all. Webland considers that Corporal Bowman, for all his shouts and showmanship, deserves the praise he strives so hard for. The men mock him behind his back. Yet how much better for everyone that he does so strive, instead of being, like so many, merely browned off.

A week has gone by and, apart from Corporal Bowman's original murderous reference, no man has discussed Webland's parentage with him. A survey of the airmen on his course has indicated three of nearly his own age whose tastes and manners are most agreeable to him. But, as he is beginning to learn, when you are on a hard course there is a smoothing spirit about which takes care of foolish prejudices and antipathies. If not such a gay band of men as the squad at Cadstone, those in the hut and in the class work harmoniously together.

These three gradually make a four with Webland at visiting the Naffy, the cinema, or the billiard table; Paul and Eric from Yorkshire and Frank from Birmingham, all making their ways in commerce, and as good a set of chaps as one could find. The comradeship speeds the weeks of the course with laughter and friendly competition.

It is Eric, an amateur of the folly of catchwords, who has coined the washing verb 'to bloot'; and it is he who, with Webland, devises paraphrases for the airman's ubiquitous: 'You've had it.' 'You have already obtained it,' says Webland. 'It has been previously procured,' caps Eric.

They please themselves also with predicting Corporal Bowman's jargonic jocularities, ingested from R.A.F. and radio chatter and reproduced with stupefying monotony: 'Okeydoke.' 'There's no future in it.' 'What's this in aid of?' 'That's pretty ropey.' And the phrase to end all questions: 'There's a war on, you know!' Corporal Bowman works them all and Eric and Webland re-work them afterwards.

At the next P.T. interval between classes, Webland and a few others claim the privilege of thirty-five-year-olds and are excused. Instead they are found the penal job of seeking salvage round about the camp buildings, which means gathering up revolting objects from the sodden ground and sorting them with bare hands into heaps. It is some consolation to the scavengers to learn later that the P.T. had come to an untimely dismissal when a tall young airman playing at wrestling had dislocated a knee and been taken away to hospital.

To replace the five finished airmen, five more arrive from Swanton, all of them of course known to Webland. Davis is much cheered to be joined by his particular friends Lloyd, Twankey Jones and Griffiths. Webland is especially fond of home-sick Griffiths who says, soon after his arrival, in his dulcet North Wales accent: 'Webland, I was neffer so glad to see anyone in my life as when I saw you.'

The second Saturday brings the lights and music on at 6 instead of 6.15; stepping up the pace, perhaps. To the Corporal's shout of 'Wakey, Wakey!' and 'Rise and Shine!', the groaning lines of sleepy airmen heave themselves up and go padding off with soap, razor and towel to the ablutions. The routine is well set by days of custom. Breakfast, only 150 yards away, is at seven o'clock, the first man out of the hut taking with him the can which he fills up with tea from a great winch-operated cauldron in the cook-house; then back to the hut with the tea-can, and getting down to sweeping and polishing for the Saturday inspection at 10.30.

Corporal Bowman selects what he calls a Senior Man of the hut; not a bad idea, thinks Webland, since the man chosen is one of his closest friends, Eric, who is thenceforward referred to as 'Senior'. His task is to help the

Corporal in such matters as laundry, the nightly blackout, tidiness and general discipline.

In quasi-naval phraseology it can be called a 'happy hut' and perhaps therefore it is an efficient hut. Certainly Senior is efficient, and his wits and capabilities are reinforced by a degree of personal charm unusual in a man who stands no higher than five feet one inch. He needs no bombast, as small men often do, to add to his stature. Corporal Bowman has again therefore proved himself a man of perception, though he never can win Senior's respect after his changed attitude of urbanity towards Webland. This, Senior says, has disgusted all those who had heard the Corporal's greeting before he had established Webland's identity. Suspected snobbery they loathe.

On the night of his uncelebrated birthday Webland is allotted the diversion of fire picquet duty. This is nominally to watch for and extinguish fires caused by enemy aircraft, but in fact it is laying and lighting fires in rooms in and about the radio school, making the beds of a Corporal, a Sergeant and an Officer, and cleaning and tidying anything seen to be out of place. Given suitable comrades firewatching can provide plenty of merriment. Webland is given them, and it does. Exhausted with toil and laughter at these night antics, the firewatchers are permitted to spend some of the remaining hours of the long night sleeping in their uniforms on spare beds in an unfamiliar hut. An early arising and a final sweeping up before 8.30 bring about their relief by another airman. The new day being Sunday there is no more set work to be done until Monday morning.

A young Irish Sergeant at the Radio School, who treats his pupils with uncommon politeness, gives Webland praise and encouragement when he meets him in the camp one day. Although some of the men are already saying half jokingly: 'Old Webland's our Star Turn', 'He's a wizard at it' and 'You ask Webland; he knows how to do it' – much as had been said of him at Cadstone – he had not believed that he and electronics could ever become on familiar terms. Speed and accuracy are the chief qualifications for the job, so the practical work comes easily and almost as enjoyably as playing at sight very simple pieces on the piano. The theoretical, too, is beginning to clarify and stick in the memory. The teachers, and the teaching so intelligently set out that a dunce can understand it, are of course responsible. Everyone is expected to win his sparks and generally does so. The sign of having become a trained Radio Operator is a small piece of black stuff picturing a fist clutching jagged radiations of light blue electricity that a man sews upon the arm of his tunic. Webland is looking forward to this technical distinction; therefore, to hear from the Sergeant that his practical work is the best in the class of twenty is good news indeed.

Another cause for satisfaction occurs that second week. Corporal Bowman, about to take a week's leave, ordains that the hut should elect a Deputy Senior Man to help Eric in the Corporal's absence. By vote of all the men the choice falls on Webland, and his nickname very soon becomes 'Dep'. This is very much more satisfactory than being appointed to the post by the Corporal, if indeed he had had a mind himself to choose Webland.

Yet another blow, no less sharp for being half expected, strikes Davis, who has been spending abominable days picking up rubbish about the camp. He has been posted to Northumberland and departs from a sympathetic hut at six in the morning with tears in his eyes and such a lump in the throat that the word 'Cheerio' can scarcely be heard. Coming three days after the arrival of his chum Griffiths makes the event doubly cruel.

'Inci*dentally*,' says Eric who seldom turns a poor pun from his door, 'the poor fellow has gone without his teeth.' These had arrived for him only the previous day and were of such a size and shape, having a kind of fantastical winged appearance, that, as Davis had said, 'with a bit of encouragement they'll take off and fly to the cookhouse by themselves.' He left them behind on his bed.

The problem of washing in comparative comfort has troubled Webland at every R.A.F. station. At last at Bindover he finds a bath that seems little used and will fill rapidly with scalding water. The discovery cheers his early mornings greatly, and he is always the first up and off to this treasure every morning. The other men don't seem to want that form of rich men's daily luxury and at such an hour. Having learnt at Swanton that there are never any plugs in such baths, he has bought for himself a large rubber disc that covers all sizes of waste hole: a most precious possession.

He has also learnt at Bindover that a man who washes in a basin and doesn't swill it clean afterwards has been ill brought up and is something of a public enemy. No one had taught him this at home where invisible hands had always dealt with such cleanings.

A rumour flashes round one evening that the authorities have devised a means of depriving the men of any remaining minutes of peace to themselves. Sports kit is to be issued so that youths' horse-play and organized games shall be the lot of all. The older ones, of whom Webland is by at least a year the oldest, are dismayed and decide to exercise their medical right to be excused. Senior is only thirty-two, so is not qualified to protest; nor are Paul and Frank. Webland used sometimes to wonder why he was always the oldest in his squads and classes and supposes that he had been called up before his time because of his worrying the local Labour Exchange last summer about when he was going to be needed.

The sports rumour develops into something more substantial when a powerful-looking Flight Sergeant orders all huts to produce lists of men, who are to be forced to choose between Rugger, Soccer, Boxing, Fencing, Lawn Tennis and Cross-country Running. This would be calamitous for those quiet half-hours for study, reading, or writing home. But the next morning the ill-favoured man returns to announce that the Warrant Officer, after everything had been organized, had forgotten to say that the edict only applied to Radio Mechanics, not to Radio Operators whose course was all too short to spare any time from concentrated studies. The elderly stout ones smile again.

At every camp there are men with tales to tell of sorrow and corruption. While Webland is waiting one morning for the newspaper car to arrive at its usual selling point, he is joined by an airman in his radio class with whom he hasn't had much previous talk. He is a quiet short dark man of working-class parentage, in his middle thirties, going bald, dull, inoffensive and uncomplaining. Being well out of his depth at the lectures, he will probably fail in the examination, get put, like the cleverer but luckless Davis, on to General Duties, sink to the bottom, and get drained away into nonentity. He always looks so cheerless that Webland thinks it well to engage him in light conversation. Webland's role is that of listener, and what he hears gives him one more reminder of his own fortune. The tale doesn't take long to tell, for the small man is not eloquent and the newspaper van is approaching. Just before being called up he had lost his wife, his daughter and his home, and he has left to him now his five-year-old remaining child boy and his old dad at Chester. What cheer for him?

Eric has a tale of enterprise to tell of how he had managed to pass the time of waiting between square-bashing and being posted to Bindover. He had spent some days scrubbing floors and peeling potatoes and was beginning to feel a little distraught; so he asked one of the less unreasonable N.C.O.s whether he couldn't find him a more congenial occupation. 'What's in it for me?' said the N.C.O. It turned out to be five shillings. Learning that he had been a Tax Inspector, the N.C.O. then asked him if he could write. Eric admitted that he could. 'Well, we'll have to bloody see.' The N.C.O. saw; and the result was that Eric soon found himself on loan to a Y.M.C.A., organizing Dominion airmen's welfare, and finally compering variety shows at the local theatre. For the loss of five shillings he spent a more interesting seven months of waiting for the radio course than the Cadtonians had at Swanton.

As the radio course proceeds so the composition of the hut changes. After three weeks, midway through, something over half of the thirty or so men in M33 hut are in the same lecture class as Webland. The rest are doomed men who have dropped out through some physical frailty, or those recently arrived and in their first or second week, or a few in their last week soon due to leave and make way for new arrivals. So the human contents of each hut change bit by bit, and completely every six weeks.

A short examination on the theoretical side of the work is held at the Radio School at the end of each week, and Webland finds he has managed to keep among the top three or four. At the practical working he is still judged the best. If his commission had come through now he would have been rather disappointed. His intimate liking for the cathode ray tube and his new-born interest in all things that move at 186 thousand and something miles a second make it imperative that he should not be taken away before he has had the chance to prove himself worthy to flaunt a zig-zag spark on his sleeve.

Still no word comes from the Air Ministry for him or for any of his applying comrades. All agree with the remark to one of them by an Officer that it is decidedly easier to get commissioned before entering the R.A.F. than ever it is once you are in. As another example among many, there is a dignified Welsh school-teacher in Webland's hut, who had been strongly recommended for a commission by his Group Captain and turned down by the Ministry Board. It is an endless puzzle and topic of talk among the aspirants whether one gets turned down because of one's provincial accent or one's athletic gaucherie.

But among the old Cadstonians and Swantonian Welsh the talk is often of tooth- and eye-cursed Davis whose letters from Northumberland have cast their sympathetic Celtic spirits down into the vasty deep.

The hut radio, with its tireless jazz and news, no longer bothers Webland. One or two of the melodies have become almost comradely in the genial human atmosphere. He can even look with benevolent interest at airmen's reaction to the music, as two of the younger ones sit close to the loudspeaker entranced, nodding, swaying, tapping their booted feet and making drummer's knocks with a comb or a fork on their bedsteads.

Three or four new arrivals, come to fill the empty beds, sit lost and listless, not knowing what to do on their first evening. No one has greeted them. One, particularly forlorn, sits staring for half an hour at the wall, and Webland, an old hand now after three weeks, hazards a few words of welcome. They might help to ease that first, fierce homeless rupture.

His watch has broken its mainspring, and Senior, knowing how important it is for him to get off to his morning bath before the bellowing Corporal bursts in at 6.10, makes a point of coming over to his bedside every night and placing his own wrist-watch beside him. Good old Senior.

After long usage by Webland and previous occupants of the bed, clean sheets arrive on Good Friday. Somebody is managing the vast camp on decent lines. In spite of certain inevitable tyrannies and injustices and omissions, most things seem to get followed up and attended to. Those sheets will doubtless be inherited by some weary, untrained airman when in three weeks' time Webland will have gone home for his seven days' leave with strange secrets in his head and those magical sparks stitched on his sleeve.

As the fourth week progresses, news comes that a dozen more old Swanton comrades are due next Thursday. Webland wonders if Adam will be among them or whether he has succeeded in getting himself re-mustered into a musician. Much as he hopes to see him again, he hopes more that he has found his way into a suitable occupation.

Thursday comes, and at half-past six in the evening there is the haggard batch tottering up to the huts with handbags and kit-bags, famished and fatigued, just as Webland and his batch had done such a seemingly long time ago. Skelding and Twankey Jones and he run out to greet them, help them and tell them the 'gen'. There among them are Phil Jones, and David Jenkins, for which much thanks.

Jenkins, of course, has a tale to tell. He says that Thomas had come away from Swanton with a substantial and illegal quantity of camp rations in his handbag. At the London terminus Service Police and N.C.O.s were there to search all airmen's baggage. Quick as a flash Thomas called out: 'I must see an Officer at once.' 'There's no Officer here,' they said, 'you better see the Sergeant.' 'No. I insist on seeing an Officer. My wife is desperately ill and if I miss that train over there that leaves in two minutes I won't answer for the consequences.' His very natural alarm lent true emotion to his false words. The compassionate Corporals made way, hurried him through uninspected and wished him all the best.

What jabber and laughter there is that night. With friends on ahead of one, everything can be mollified and jollified; without them at one's first arrival death would seem merciful.

Next day, wet clothes and cold winds at last get the better of Webland, so that he shivers and longs to be in bed at home. Lacking domestic comfort, human comfort does its best. One man gives him aspirins, another presses on him a concoction of port and brandy, and he struggles to bed at seven. Rapid recovery is essential, with the end of the course in sight and every hour of training priceless.

In the morning, with the encouragement of his comrades, he manages to get up, to make his bed rather less neatly than usual, leaving buttons and boots uncleaned, and to march, more or less, up to the Radio School. There the Corporal Instructor, observing his poor state, refrains from chivvying him and allows him to sit for four or five hours in his overcoat in a warm corner of the room listening to what is going on and doing no practical work. One more early long night he is sure will beat this chill.

One of the airmen tells him of an old remedy for a sore throat: to sleep with your dirty socks round your neck. The effect of the treatment is miraculous, for the next day the fever is gone and the terror of reporting sick nothing but a past nightmare.

Skelding, who had applied for a commission at the same time as Webland, reports to his fellow applicants that according to his brother-in-law at the Air Ministry, there is such a formidable muddle with the commissions, nobody knowing who had applied when, that there are no vacancies anywhere except in the Catering Branch, and they expect a years wait for all Officers.

This news has its calculated depressive effect upon the few concerned. Webland finds it hard to believe, but he has begun to think that there may be some delay over his own case when he hears from Cuthbert Latimer that it is considered at the Ministry that he stands a good chance of promotion if he should prove competent at some coming job which he has not yet heard of. In the R.A.F. it seems that if you are commissioned it has to be in some Branch or Trade. But what Branch or Trade is Webland yet fitted for? He has proved competent at recruit drill, even at P.T. and combat, and he is about to prove competent at Radio Operations. What further tests of skill or virtue are required of him before being judged worthy of the royal trust. What is the real meaning of it all? Why is he here? Where and what is he meant to be?

But always, when he feels depressed, he has only to look about him to see others in worse cases. There is the Welsh school-teacher whose scholarship and honours degree at the University of Wales have counted for nothing in his application. This friendly scholar observes in Webland the same lukewarm quality noted by Adam, only under another name. 'I never saw a man with such placidity as yours, Dep.' And how beautifully he pronounced the word 'placidity'.

More bad luck and disappointment, also, are to be seen among the new intake from Swanton when two of them are turned down, as Davis had been, before the course began, for bad eyesight, to be almost certainly posted away.

Four weeks of the course have passed and only a vestige of Webland's fever and sore throat remain. He feels well enough to put in for a 36-hour pass to spend Saturday night with friends in the next county. The pass is allowed; but there is the usual obstruction in the way of procuring it, for it can only be collected, and in person, at the Squadron Office between the hours of 8 and 12.30, which whole period he and his class are to spend at the Radio School. Although such rules are unalterable, N.C.O.s' hearts can bend them, and the Sergeant at the school lets him be dismissed at 12.15 so that he can just get his pass in time. That may have been done as a reward for his diligence, because at the weekly examination of theory two days before he had once more come out among the top three.

The twenty-five mile journey, such as Webland would have made in his own car in thirty to forty minutes, takes him just under six hours, but that slow performance can be ascribed to his lack of practice in opportunist travelling. How valuable is each minute when the leave pass is limited to a few hours, and how devastating are the waits and disappointments of journeying, as it were, on trust.

From the Radio School at 12.15 to the Squadron Office; from the camp at 1.20 by bus to the nearest town four miles in the wrong direction; from that town a twenty-minute ride by bus, standing, to a town six miles in the right direction; an hour and a half there before catching the 3.40 train to another town twenty-one miles in the right direction; it goes, however, to a different town fourteen miles instead of four miles distant from his destination; reckless now about the cost, he begs a taximan to drive him those fourteen miles, but the taximan refuses; walking seems the wisest, if the only, method then; but there comes a bus which carries him a mile, until two newspaper deliverers take him along in their van a few miles farther, on the way shying out bundles of evening papers at collecting boys and over garden fences; with only two miles to go he hasn't advanced 200 yards before an old man takes him in his car to the very village of his target.

He spends nearly twenty-four hours in the home of his friends, then sets off to find his way back to camp. The journey might take half or twice as long as yesterday's. He can depend upon the start, but the finish is impossible to foretell.

The drive to the railway station in the friends' car makes a capital beginning; the 5.35 to the next town ten miles away keeps to its programme and delivers him at six o'clock just in time to miss the bus that would go within three or four miles of the camp; the next one is not due to leave until 8.30; he therefore walks to the London road and swings along it as he used to swing along the old road back to Swanton, confident of being picked up very soon by a patriotic motorist. There are not many of any kind that Sunday evening, but of the dozen there are none will stop at his unprofessional hitch signs. After five miles along the road he sights to the left a hill-top monument which can be seen from Bindover, so he takes to the fields and the downs, where the grass feels good to his boots after the hammering road, and arrives at his bedside at 8.30. He had only walked between eight and nine miles, but in the fine mid-April weather it had been hot going, wearing or bearing an overcoat, haversack and respirator pack.

One of the new men from Swanton tells him that a signal had been received there a few days ago, asking for Officers to be recommended for Operations. According to the interviewing Board he had seen in London, that sounds like the job for Webland. Perhaps his records have been lost and everyone is searching for him. None of that, however, bothers him now that he is starting upon the last week of the course. Life with the goniometer in some post of responsibility, with an enemy aircraft to detect, seems just as attractive a goal as this fading Officer's commission.

Yet why stay on the ground detecting if one can get after them in the air? He hasn't much hope of success in the matter of re-mustering or of promotion, but there is a flying trade of Radio Operator/Observer, and if he can pass out well as an Operator, why should he not aspire to being an Observer as well?

He sounds the N.C.O.s at the Radio School and asks them if it isn't the case that men of forty can get accepted as Observers. They know little about it but think not. 'Are you mad keen?' they ask. He cannot pretend that he is more than hopeful of being able to do something a little more offensive than this ground work. The Sergeant replies with an assurance that there is no job more important than locating the enemy off the coast, that an interview on the subject with an Officer would be hard to procure, and that anyway he will find himself posted elsewhere next week as soon as the course is ended.

This Sergeant is the N.C.O. at the School who is chiefly responsible for judging the airmen's work. He has seldom been heard to give praise, but that afternoon, mellowed perhaps by the fact that he is going on leave the next day, he speaks leniently to Webland and one or two others who are in the room. In bidding them good-bye he wishes them luck in passing out, saying that Webland at least needn't worry. He then adds something in Webland's ear to the effect that his practical skill has been quite outstanding and that he would like to tell him more about it some time.

Webland also would like to have heard some more in that strain, but by the time the Sergeant was back from his leave Webland would be away, and they were pretty certain never to meet again. Still, whatever failures might come afterwards he would always be able to say: 'Well, as a matter of fact, I was once considered quite outstanding at the goniometer.'

'Oh? And what, may one ask, is a goniometer?'

A blackbird perched on a water pipe flutes so loud and long that evening that airmen in the hut, not too near the radio, comment on the noise. Webland goes outside to applaud and spies a usually cruel-faced Sergeant from the next hut standing motionless and plainly softened by the song. They catch one another's British eyes and retire.

Hut M33 is situated in the best part of the camp, although almost a quarter of an hour's walk from the entrance. From the doorway can be seen the fields and low hills of a very pretty landscape. Webland is now sure that in all respects life at Bindover is far superior to that at Swanton, once he has got used to the public manners of a hut. Here again he has been lucky in his companions. The occupants of the six beds up at Webland's end, which they call the Ritz, all get on particularly well together. There are three or four rather rowdy boys at the far end, who make a slight discord, but never so much as to disturb the general well being. The Corporal and the elders are in firm control.

Senior, discussing with Webland the qualities of some of the N.C.O.s at Bindover, mentions the Sergeant at the Radio School: he who had praised Webland's work and gone on leave. This Sergeant had asked Senior if Webland's father was a bloody lord, to which Senior had replied that he wasn't so sure about the adjective, but that it was so and did it make any difference? The Sergeant said: 'Oh, no.' The adjective was only a prestige support; much as a leathery American General, in the course of a sentimental parting oration, feeling his voice about to break in a sob, will throw in an inept 'Goddam' as a counterbalance: 'You're the finest goddam troops a man ever commanded.'

On the final Friday, the ultimate bullshit night arrives.

In addition to polishing his own bedspace and carefully protecting the fresh gleam with a covering of newspapers against the morrow's inspection, Webland has the duty of polishing Corporal Bowman's too. Hands' and knees' work, that. Each week one half of the men have extra tasks to do, such as shining the brasswork, cleaning the passages and the windows, or washing the centre table and its benches. There must be no letting down on the standard. One's own apparel, buttons, badge and boots follow. Only after that can come recreation and writing letters home. Webland's letter that evening is filled with the complex problem of his journey and arrival home on the following Thursday.

At the practical examination none has surpassed him. The theoretical does not come so easily. Although he has been thinking electronically for a month and can draw exactly a picture of the cathode ray tube if necessary in his sleep, he has neither the past interest nor the supple mechanism in his brain to assimilate as surely as some of the other and younger pupils. The examination paper is easy, but he knows that he has, as others confess that they have, made several mistakes and omissions. However, he is second in the result and is very well satisfied.

An Officer then addresses the class of twenty and asks for the names of any who wish to return to Bindover after their seven days' leave, take a short Instructors' course on the job and become Acting-Corporals. Fifteen put their names down, half of them lads who Webland thinks would have preferred a more adventurous life. The great dread of some of his colleagues, he learns, is of being posted to a place far from their homes and, worst of all, overseas. Afterwards it is said that the Flight Sergeant commented privately and with suitable epithets on such lack of enterprise. Senior, Paul and two others over thirty besides Webland have not volunteered to stay.

Having been in a bad state of nerves before the final examination the class displays the reaction of high spirits afterwards. In the hut the pranks threaten to get out of hand: blankets are rumpled up, pyjamas hidden, fire-extinguishers stuffed inside beds, and similar subtleties. Webland is not expected to partake, nor is the peace of his bed space disturbed.

On the last Sunday he decides to try to hire a bicycle for the purpose of visiting some people he knows in the neighbourhood. He moves in a queue from 8.30 until 10.10 when all the machines have been hired out. There is a great shoving and swearing and cheating, so that some who come last get in before those who have come earlier. As he walks bikeless away the hirer comes after him and offers him his own machine. The invitation is strangely generous, since Webland doesn't know the man. The price is 1/8d and it is a species of racing bicycle. After a meal at midday Webland springs into the saddle and pedals off for a few yards, then dismounts to look at the rear tyre. It is flat, and there is no pump; nor is there a pump or hirer to be found at the man's place of trade; so the trip is abandoned and once more bicycle money has been spent for nothing.

On the machine being returned next day, the hirer is again co-operative and offers to lend him another, either that evening or the next day, before the six o'clock opening time, so avoiding the queue, and free of further charge. That might well prove useful for a spin to the town to cash a cheque before leave, especially as three of his four boots are badly in need of cobbling, and the less walking done the better.

Signs of departure begin to appear in the hut two days in advance, for every item of equipment has to be displayed for inspection at eleven o'clock on Tuesday morning. No further work is ordained before the night shift, from 6.30 to 12.30. The previous night nothing had been demanded of them at the Radio School beyond half an hour's sweeping up.

Webland, Paul, Senior and another man from the class named Dixon, are sent for during the day to present themselves before the Officer at the School once more on the subject of becoming cut-price Instructors with Corporals' tapes but A/C2s' pay. None of the four has put his name down for this complimentary job. The Officer says that he wants the most responsible kind of men for this special task, which he assures them is at present of greater value to the war effort than going out on the chain to operate. Senior and Paul are impressed by his argument and consent to return after their leave, but Webland and Dixon say they would only do it if the Officer was positively stuck for Instructors. In the end he was not stuck, for he chose out of the class no more than seven from old and young. Webland and Dixon congratulate one another in their obstinacy and on appearing to be so desirable to the authorities.

In the afternoon his racing bicycle spins him into the town where he cashes a cheque, buys a few things and pays 12/6d in advance for a taxi to be at the camp at 7.20 on Thursday morning to take four airmen, himself, Frank, Skelding and a man from Hereford, to the local train so as to make sure of catching an important connexion for home. Such foresight, however, proves a folly and a loss, for when Webland mentions the fact to the Flight Sergeant on the night shift at the School, the Flight Sergeant replies in no polite manner that Webland needn't think that he can do that kind of thing, that going away for leave is a parade, and that every man should go on the transport and catch the proper train at the proper time.

Never mind: the course has been successfully accomplished, he is now master of a technical trade in the R.A.F., and he is going on seven days' leave home in damson blossom time. To jump the gun in a taxi as well is perhaps asking for too much.

On the last day are announced the postings. Seven men, of course, are coming back to Bindover to be Instructors. The rest of the class are to be dispersed to their R.D.F. work about the coasts; all except Webland. He is told he has been posted to Cawford. The name means nothing to him, but some of his mates, who always seem well informed about the Service, give a gasp of surprise. 'Good Lord, Dep, what are you going there for? There's no one lower than a Group Captain at that place.'

Everyone is mystified, the N.C.O.s no less so, and with an additional hint of awe. Perhaps they suspect, as Webland himself is inclined to do, that a string is being pulled. He doesn't know whether to be pleased or not. Understanding nothing of the general organization of the R.A.F. he is in no state to hold any opinion on this unusual outcome. He only knows that he will miss the old and new friends of Cadstone, Swanton and Bindover whom he has made and kept through seven months of crowded life, and that he is now to be pushed off into the blue air once more, and on his own.

Perhaps, though, there is good luck ahead. This odd posting certainly looks auspicious. But he didn't want it arranged like this. The whole object has always been for himself to demonstrate his own suitability to be an Officer.

8
Remismustered

And therfore, at the Kynge's court, my brother,
Ech man for hymself, ther is noon oother.
CHAUCER – *The Canterbury Tales*

Dischannelled, posted out of his trade stream without explanation, Webland arrives and reports at his fifth R.A.F. station. Cawford is a large camp, controlled by Fighter Command, in the metropolitan suburbs, and he can see that a leave pass of only a few hours will give him ample time to visit relations and friends in London: a prospect that illuminates some of the bleakness of the first hours of customary unwelcome.

The game of establishing identity begins at the Guard Room, thence to the Group Orderly Room where he deposits his kit-bag, to set out on a two-hour search for the Pay Accounts building, the Medical Inspection room for the stripped F.F.I., and the Respirator office to get his New Arrival paper signed.

From all this it is beginning to look as though he hasn't come here to receive an immediate commission. No one in fact can tell him why he has been posted to this place where Radio Operators are unknown. A Corporal suggests that he has been re-mustered without his knowledge to some trade yet to be revealed.

At the end of three hours he is directed to a barrack block of dormitories, each with about thirty beds along the walls and up the middle, and one of these last he appropriates. There is a locker, no bolster, and but two blankets instead of four. The few room-mates visible look to be in their teens or very early twenties. One of them shows him how to loot blankets from other beds which have accumulated five or six apiece. There is a dirty bolster on the floor which he is glad to secure, although the state of that floor would set Corporal Bowman screaming for broom, polish and bumper. The helpful room-mate is a lad of twenty who had joined the Artillery when he was sixteen, escaped from Dunkirk, and found his adventurous way into the Royal Air Force.

Webland, thoroughly depressed by his surroundings, heartily wishes he had been posted, even with some uncongenial comrade, to a coastal radio station where a new arrival would surely be less coldly received and be found some fitting work to do. But this place, for which he had set out to the applause and envy of all at Bindover, doesn't even know that it had sent for him. Perhaps it hadn't.

A temporary solution to the problem is found early next morning when he is told that he had better go home and come back in forty-eight hours, by which time something may have been discovered about him. This is gratefully accepted as an uncommonly sensible move.

Since London is so close, it seems easier on this occasion not to go home but to spend the two nights with his youngest sister Belinda at the flat she is sharing in Grosvenor Square. Their family house just round the corner had been long requisitioned by the Government. He has not had a chance of a long talk with her since the war began.

On the first evening they sit up until past midnight comparing the absurdities of their present situations and laughing back into the far past at Amberdine. Comical as she thinks Webland looks in his airman's uniform, there is nothing but admiration on his part at her ambulance costume, especially when she tells him her personal bomb story which last year had put an end to several of her companions and sent her off duty for three months' convalescence. He is grateful also to her for her understanding of his own Service life and the failure to advance his prospects.

Very different is her attitude from that of their fellow-diners the next evening at the Dorchester, when most of them take the view that he is a bit of an ass not to have 'done something about it'. Most indignant of all is Claud Marchley, chairman of one of Webland's larger Boards, who says that it's absolute rot going about looking like that and that he's going to have a word with the D.M.I. and get something fixed up for him there. The next day happens to be the date of the Company's Annual General Meeting and Webland says that he would just have time to join the Directors there before getting back to camp. Claud, however, tactfully indicates that perhaps the shareholders might be taken aback by the sight of an A/C2 on the Board, so if he were Webland he would give it a miss.

Who, he wonders, is the D.M.I? He doesn't like to show his ignorance to the jolly diners, but it is a rank that he hasn't come across in the R.A.F.

Although two years of common danger have lowered a little the subtle barriers between the several grades of social classes, to none of which Webland feels that he now belongs, he finds it difficult to re-adapt himself to the old self-confidence of privilege, and is inclined, against his nature, to be morose. He reflects how small and how great is the difference between these whose peace-time lives are marked in phrases like 'going up for the twelfth' and 'going down for the fourth' and those to whom such dates are meaningless but whose pulses quicken at thoughts of 'going up for the cup' and 'going down for the count'. Like so much else that divides mankind, it is basically a matter of wealth. After the war the barriers will be raised again.

On his return to Cawford it is apparent that not much detective progress on his past and future had been made. At nine o'clock in the morning, after having given his buttons and boots a very good polish, he presents himself at the Operations Room to wait until the Flight Sergeant and the Officer are ready for him. He sits on a chair while many operators, male and female, come in and out and put on and take off headphones for their plotting jobs round the vast table map. After an hour he gives up his chair to one of the operators and stands for another hour, during which time he picks up a pencil for a Waaf and gives a light for a cigarette to another. The work going on is interesting to watch, by reason of its novelty. Small coloured metal arrow-heads are moved by means of long magnetic rods from square to square on the map to represent the position of flying aircraft.

A young Squadron Leader comes in and mounts the dais or gallery overlooking the plotters, where sit the Controller, Officers and others.

The Flight Sergeant beckons Webland upstairs and says: 'This is that Radio Operator.'

The Officer says to Webland: 'What are you here for?'

'I don't know, sir.'

The Officer and the Flight Sergeant busy themselves with some work for about a quarter of an hour, when he hears the Flight Sergeant say: 'What shall I do with this man?'

The answer to these seven awful words Webland cannot hear.

'Come back here at nine o'clock tomorrow morning,' says the Flight Sergeant.

Passes out of camp are easily obtained, so Webland boards an Underground train and lunches at his Club, where he observes the Chief of the Air Staff also enjoying an hour off from his more exacting duties. He returns at sunset.

So lag the morning and the evening of the third day. It is the first week in May and the weather is beginning to feel warm from inside the thick shirt, underclothes and tunic.

Sleep is hard to come by in a bed in the centre of the

dormitory. The young come in late, full of familiar oaths and crude pornologies, bumping past Webland's bed and punctuating their remarks with windy body noises.

Next day Webland, hopeful once more, rises at six, finds his way to a plugless bath which no longer thwarts him, breakfasts at seven and reports to the Ops Room at nine. He sits on a stool in a passage until ten-fifteen, then stands outside the young Squadron Leader's door until eleven forty-five. The Officer still knows nothing and tells Webland to go and ask the Orderly Room to look up his papers again. The Orderly Room finds a paper saying that he is to be trained in the Operations Room to be a Controller: that is to say an Officer.

So this is it. Six months after his interview at the Air Ministry they have found him and put him back on the right track. *Readiness at Dawn* is coming true at last. He has seen the Ops Room, the map, the arrows and the headphones, the Officers on the dais, and now he is to learn their duties and particularly those of the junior Officer known as Ops B. At present he feels like Ops Z for Zero.

So back with the news to the Ops Room and to report to the Flight Sergeant in charge. He knows nothing of Webland's posting and duties; nor does the Squadron Leader; nor does the Wing Commander. He is therefore returned to the Orderly Room to tell them that nothing can be done for him and that he must have been posted to the wrong command. In place of the morning's sunshine of fresh hope and progress there now appears on the horizon something that looks very much like an extensive cumulus of fatigues ahead. The situation must clear up soon.

On his way between the Ops and Orderly Rooms lies a great barrack square upon which a mass of airmen are obviously learning to be both armed and unarmed combatants. A familiar voice and figure directs their activities with the savagery that used to delight the civilians on the cliff walk at Cadstone. Later in the day at the Naffy over a glass of ale ex-Sergeant Daly, who instantly recognizes his star pupil, recounts the story of his downfall. He seems pleased to talk to Webland, who is gratified to know that out of many thousands he had taught, this apparently slow witted ring-fighter has not forgotten him.

It had truly been Daly who had sold the passes for ten shillings each to the recruits, but it seems that the brain and the itching palm behind had been those of the Warrant Officer, the Chief Drill Instructor, that model of elegance and exactitude of whom all were so much in awe. At the Court Martial Daly had uttered no word to implicate his patron, and, as he said to Webland, he had 'carried the can back for the bastard'. As he had passed 'the bastard', after the judgement on his way to degradation and ninety-one days in the glass-house, he had received from him no sign, nor had done since, of recognition. Now Daly was an L.A.C., expecting to become a Corporal, and was teaching Service Policemen how to fight rough.

Whether it is the sorrow and the squalor of this tangential contact with crime and its consequences, or the second-hand taste of the air in the passages and Ops Room, Webland is conscious that evening of a headache and a stuffiness and a sweating and a shivering, which intensify as the night wears on. He has been ordered to attend certain shifts, or watches, in the Ops Room until further notice. He asks leave of the Corporal to go back to bed, and the Corporal would have given it, but the Flight Sergeant says he must stay on duty until seven in the morning and then if he is no better report sick at eight.

Perish the thought. He'll perish first. Some aspirin and a good sleep from 7.30 until 3 will freshen him up for the next watch from 4 until 8. Another night's sleep, then on again at 7 a.m., by which time he should be perfectly well.

It seems to be something of a favour that he is allowed

to start learning Ops work at all, for they still say that they don't know what he's meant to be doing here. After reporting back to the Orderly Room he had been sent to the Pilot Officer at Signals, for whom he had waited from 2.30 until 4.40. In spite of the sparks upon his arm, of which he is still proud, the Signals Officer had taken no interest in him. So the Ops Room finally had had to accept him.

Where there are Ops Rooms, Radio Operators and Radio Telephone Operators, there are Waafs. Hitherto Webland had never worked among them. He was of course familiar with the much quoted phrase, by which the genus Waaf was satirized. When asked what she does, her reply is supposed to be: 'Aim in Ops, ectually.' And here they were, if not saying it, living it.

Among these girls at Cawford, by a stroke of luck, was an old though somewhat younger friend and neighbour of Webland's family, Vera Downton, the widow of a pilot who had been drowned in the North Sea at the beginning of the war. Many of the Officers in the Command had been friends of her husband. She had been a Waaf plotter in Ops for some time and, hearing of his arrival, she had sent him a note to say that she would do what she could to help him. Her knowledge of the Service and her acquaintance with some of the Officers in the Group, as well as her gay conversation, were going to make Cawford less of a blur during this fresh period of probation.

Next morning he is congratulating himself on having vanquished the short fever when he observes on his body a slight eruption of spots. Fleas again, he thinks, remembering the consequences of the flea of Glanville. After many inquiries he finds out where to have his blankets fumigated and exchanged, a little over a mile away from the barrack block. If he can buy some flea powder he should be able to repel further attacks.

There will be no difficulty about getting out to the shops, for by the cycle of shifts worked in Ops there is a

great deal of time allowed out on passes. This Wednesday
to Saturday, for example, the first watch is from 7 a.m.
to noon; the second from 8 p.m. to midnight; the third
from noon to 4 p.m.; the fourth from midnight to 7 a.m.;
the fifth from 4 p.m. to 8 p.m.; the sixth and last from
7 a.m. to noon. Such a spell, in the close and artificial
atmosphere and lighting, is calculated to be arduous
enough to merit a 56-hour leave pass, which means home,
if one can reach and afford it, every eight or nine days.

All this and much else is explained by Vera at their
first and subsequent meetings. She is discovered by Webland among her colleagues, looking very neat and pretty
in her uniform, and is evidently popular with everyone.
She introduces him to her Sergeant, called Betty, and
to a few other friends, who all seem to speak with the
Ops accent. Vera is interested in his adventures and conditions and insists on giving him a green pillow-slip for his
greasy bolster, though he refuses her offer of sheets as well.

The spots aren't behaving as they should. They are
developing in a fashion outside his experience of fleadom.
He decides, therefore, to go and see a doctor in London.
A telephone call to his sister furnishes him with the
name and address of Dr McGregor in Pont Street, and
as soon as the watch ends at noon he is off to settle the
matter during the period before the 8 to midnight watch.

The doctor hears his tale, inspects the spots, feels his
neck, and says: 'Chicken-pox. You must have caught it
about three weeks ago.' That means Bindover. He
wonders how many of his radio friends have caught it
too. He also wonders if he can get home, and, if he can,
if he should. Being an infectious disease it has probably
been given already to sundry airmen, Waafs, travellers
and club lunchers, and the sooner he gets himself into
isolation the better. This, in the circumstances of military
law, can only mean one thing: reporting sick.

He is surprised to find, now that he knows what is
wrong and has decided what to do, that he is not as much
dejected as he would have thought. The first week has

been a depressing one, and now that he is beginning to be accepted, to forget that he is really a Radio Operator and to be interested in the new kind of work, here it is all brought to a halt again. Also, of course, there will be no 56-hour leave on Saturday.

That morning on duty the Flight Sergeant, the one who had not allowed him to go to bed on the night when he had felt ill, had said that he wanted a word with him outside the Ops Room. He had then apologized for asking who he was, but people were talking, Officers too, and, in fact, was he Lord Webland's son? Having got the desired reply he had said: 'Well, anything I can do to help you . . .' and so on. A little late, perhaps, but still welcome. It was a pity to have to throw it all up now that he was beginning to settle down and enjoy the work. The sleeping accommodation, however, he was not enjoying at all.

On his journey back to Cawford after seeing Dr McGregor, he is feeling ill enough to be glad that he is going to give in and report sick. At the M.I. room he waits for half an hour watching orderlies making bawdy knockabout among themselves until the young Medical Officer is ready to receive him.

'I think it's chicken-pox, sir.'

'That's for me to say.'

For his own sake Webland blurted out his diagnosis, half fearing that he might get another certificate of *Pediculosis*. N.Y.D.

Thank heaven, though, the M.O. gets this one right. Varicella it is. But before the ambulance comes for him there is work to do. He has to pack up the remainder of his belongings ready to be fumigated. A young acquaintance in the barrack agrees to send a telegram home for him giving the address at Stopfield R.A.F. Hospital, where he has been told he's bound for, and to forward any letters for him there. This hospital has the initials I.D.H. attached to it, and that stands for Infectious Diseases Hospital.

So, into the ambulance and on to a comfortable stretcher, alongside a gay boy with incipient scarlet fever and apparently no cares at all, Webland feels more buoyant with every mile that takes him away from those grisly Cawford sleeping quarters. Whatever the hospital may be like it can hardly be worse than those.

The driver races through the streets and out into the darkening countryside, an eye every few miles to his wrist-watch, clanging the big bell, and is as pleased as Punch on their arrival to find he has made the twenty-five miles in thirty-seven minutes. He may just have beaten the record.

A doctor comes out of the main hospital to check up the passengers and send them on another half-mile to the isolation building. Here a Sister conducts him into a clean bright room for one, where he undresses and sinks into a sheeted bed with a sense of relief unknown to him since he first wore uniform.

The short night ends soon after 5 a.m., in hospital fashion, with orders to wash in bed: a long and gymnastical task. That done he lies back, smiling at his good fortune and surveying the butter-coloured walls, brown linoleum, bedside carpet, basin and dressing-table. Outside the wide windows he can see green and yellow meadows and hazy hills at the prime of the year. Never before has he had a feeling of such positive relaxation as now when he reflects that he is legitimately away from the ranks and the huts and the canteens, the cigarette smoke, the swearing and the radio, for three weeks in this paradise, with almost certainly a super-paradise week at home to follow.

Typical of the kind of silly strain under which he had been compressing himself on scores of occasions in this service life, had been a trivial adventure on his last trip to London. Trying to buy a travelling bag in one of the big stores for his wife's birthday, he had chosen one and was told by the shop assistant that such bags could only be bought by Officers. He now perceived that such kinds of absurdity confronting him a few times every day for a few months are likely to add up to a state bordering upon nervous frustration, not less real for being temporarily obscured. This break, then, has come none too soon, and when it is over he will set about winning that commission with restored vigour.

The young man in the ambulance, an armourer named Tomkins, having been rediagnosed as not having scarlet fever, comes to the door to say good-bye before being returned to Cawford. He says that there's a sick Waaf in the next room, and that the Sister had muttered as she came out:

'I'd rather look after a dozen men than one woman.'

All his kit has been taken away and even the letters he writes have to have the corners of the envelopes cut off to smoke the infection out of them. He wears a dwarf's suit of pyjamas. Are they not supposed to have any big patients at military hospitals? Apart from this imperfection, the 5 a.m. self wash, and the obstruction of the many spots on his head and body, he is utterly contented and feeling perfectly well. The food is succulent and the nurses charming.

'Would you like cocoa or Ovaltine or anything else?' they had asked him on the night of his arrival. He had almost forgotten how to make a choice. And on the second day:

'Well, getting bored with your own company?'

Little does she know. Outside are trees and hedges in blossom, birds are singing, and there's nothing whatever to worry about.

Thinking, perhaps, that he really will be bored so long alone, or, more likely, to solve a problem of accommodation, on the third day they move him down the passage into a room with three other airmen, all young. They look pleasant lads, and spots are good social barrier-breakers. But he misses the view from his other window, and the privacy.

In the next bed lies an anxious Corporal. He feels ill

and has left his pencil in the tunic that has gone to be baked. As he begins to feel better he talks more and he tells Webland that not long ago he was stationed at Lossiemouth, for five days only. It was for such a short time because, when he reported for duty there, he found that his squadron had returned to Suffolk a week before he had been posted. It is satisfying for Webland to be reminded that he is not the only juggins who gets misposted, mismustered and mishandled.

The first inspection takes place next morning. A Group Captain doctor, a Wing-Commander, a Squadron Leader Canadian doctor and the topmost Matron of the main hospital come round. According to the custom in the Service, all books and extras that are not in the list of inspectables have to be hidden in beds and under mattresses, while each patient sits up tidily at attention in his bed. Hair should be neatly brushed, but Webland's cannot be because it is still matted from calamine lotion on the dozen spots somewhere in the thin tangle of his scalp. All four in the room pass the inspection.

Vera has written a sympathetic letter telling him that she has had a talk about him with Squadron Leader Malvern. When he comes back to Cawford, he should go to the Flight Sergeant and ask to see Malvern who would like to know how he is situated and whether he can help him. She adds that she and Webland are to be put on the same watch.

He has also had an even more welcome letter from Adam, whom he had left last March in a state half of labourer half of musician at Swanton, and to whom he had written weeks ago.

'I did miss your company and I think everyone did. I am often accosted by airmen, strangers to me, who inquire about you and if I know how you are getting on. Your name is often mentioned at the radio room, where we have quite a bunch of new boys who seem to do nothing. . . . Have no idea what will happen to me – understand I am now a musician but must remain labouring meantime. . . . We have much to be thankful for: no fires of course but plenty of coal if we were allowed to burn it; the same old threats – notices are stuck on doors, but they seldom come to anything. The same horse and cart live above, thumping on our ceiling. The helpful little cook has gone. The food remains the same – same sand; it has lasted well. I slave just as before – expert with the truck, the postal job and so on, always hearing: "Oi! Oi!, you!", but I become a new man as I march up the road to the Railway Station with my 48-hours ticket of leave.

'I hope you are having a happier time now and will keep clear of the evil ignorant element which thrives in the Service. Trust you are well and forgetting the whole darn'd nightmare. Your letter has recalled the only pleasant time I've spent in the R.A.F. Everything still looks unchanged, but the atmosphere changed completely for me when you left. I've been instructed by all the boys to send you "All the best".'

The hospital days pass quickly, one being much like another for the four agreeable room-mates; only the Corporal has had the disease at all severely. After little more than a week the Senior Sister hints that the three recovering ones may be released within three or four days.

'Shall we be allowed to go home, Sister?'

'Oh, yes, certainly.'

'For how long?'

'Five days at least, I should think.'

The close future does not look bad. It seems as though, on his return from convalescence, he is going to have quite an interesting job at Cawford with plenty of leave passes thrown in. After he has had his talk with Squadron Leader Malvern, from whom he had no great expectations, he is not going to worry about the commission any more. It is obvious that the system is unmanageable. If preferment can only be got by popping in behind private doors and supplicating influential personages, then let it go. The hand of Cuthbert has diverted his career as far as this and little good has come of it.

There is merriment when the three patients clothe themselves for the first time in their hospital blues. First come a vest half an inch thick and shaped like a sack, anomalously normal drawers, and a huge white canvas shirt down to the knees; then round the collar goes a wide and shapeless band of a red tie; bright blue tubular serge trousers held up by a pyjama tape through the hem of the waist; and a blue jacket made for a smallish Waaf.

Clad thus they venture out and lie on the grass in the sunshine, not without having first been roared at by a Flight Sergeant for some infringement of rule he fancied they were making in not carrying respirators. The foolish fellow is quite at fault, and one of Webland's comrades groans: 'Oh, God, back to R.A.F. insults once more.'

It is to be a week's leave for them all next Tuesday, after twelve happy days of sickness.

Tuesday arrives and the leave is true. It comes and goes like a lovely dream. It is now the end of May and he reports back again at Cawford in search of a bed to sleep in.

He knows no one in the barrack, and the effort of making friends has to begin all over again. One of these beds in the middle of the long room, the newcomers' area, is empty and will have to do. Beneath it, at least, there is a wooden box which can be padlocked.

He is getting to know some of his colleagues in the Ops Room, three of whom are a schoolmaster, a solicitor and a jockey, the jockey seeming to Webland, who knows nothing of the turf, a most delightful fellow. It seems that Ops airmen are picked from the more refined trades and professions, but that doesn't make the spirit of the place any better than at other camps; perhaps less good. He still misses his first Cadstone friends: Shag, the convict; Stan, the truck driver; George, the sailor; above all Corporal Cowley and the comical Welsh clique.

During the night watch in the Ops Room a junior

Officer tells him that he got his own commission after seven months in the ranks. He has been an Officer now for three months, although he had been accepted some time after the date of Webland's acceptance. He is much younger, has no particular qualifications, no influence nor any strings to pull. Promotion looks more than ever like a lucky dip, and this man one of the rare prize winners.

Webland continues to wonder why he is not much attracted to any of his colleagues here. Is he getting tired of the ranks and therefore of everybody in them, or is it the undoubted fact that these are, or act at being, more selfish than any others he has hitherto been thrown among? The cause of that may be not so much that they are a bad lot as that most of them are disappointed men: men who had begun and sometimes got far on their courses towards flying duties and then been struck off by some mental or physical shortcoming. On being transferred to terrestrial tasks their reception hasn't always been sympathetic. Already smouldering with grief and anger at their descent, they become objects for mockery by certain meaner N.C.O.s.

'Yer thought yerselves the cream of the Service, didn't yer? Now look at yer! Well, the cream's gone sour, hasn't it, and yer better toe the line with the rest . . .'

However browned off these lads may be, the best thing for Webland is to concentrate on what there is to be learnt by studying and asking questions about the work round the great map; and here Vera with her jokes and knowledge is invaluable. She can't understand why Squadron Leader Malvern hasn't had his promised talk with him and he asks her not to mention it.

At breakfast one morning he finds himself sitting among a group of airmen who have been posted to Cawford to learn how to become Service Policemen, straight from their square-bashing on the west coast. After three days here it has been discovered that they aren't tall enough, so they are waiting to be sent about the country as G.D.s, labouring. Being comparatively new to the Service they bear their relegation with smiling fortitude.

Having made one move of billets already, the word gets round that he and his fellow watchers are to make another, to wooden huts close to the Ops Room. Their present hut is constructed of stone and is therefore less permeable by the heat of the sun. June has come and with it very much warmer weather. No one wants to move, although there is some advantage in moving nearer to the cook-house.

It is difficult to get information about prospects, but someone has told Webland that before he can get a look at a commission in this line he will have to pass a Trade Test in Ops, in the same way that aircraftmen and Waafs have to do when they re-muster to a fresh branch. If this is so he feels peeved that he should have been sent to Bindover to take the six weeks' radio course, which of course he had never been intended for in the first place and now be expected to learn a mass of detail that is said to take most airmen six months to assimilate.

Some illumination comes from Frank Mead, whom Webland has arranged to see in London. Whether or not a Squadron Leader is behaving correctly in sharing a table with an aircraftman at the Mayfair Hotel, Webland doesn't know and Frank doesn't care. Overworked as he is, Frank explains how the system is supposed to function. That Webland is now on the way to being commissioned in Operations seems to be as much owing to Frank as to Cuthbert; for Frank has spoken more than once to Fighter Command H.Q. about getting hold of him. He had asked them first as long ago as last September and they had said that that was the kind of man wanted as an Ops Officer; but for months they had lost him in the machinery. Now that he has been found, Frank says, all will be plain sailing. There will be about ten days more at Cawford; then will come a few weeks at a station in the Home Counties, an examination, and by about September he should be on his six weeks' officers' square-bashing course.

Frank is the Senior Controller at his Sector and he knows most of the Officers who count in these matters and fears none of them, so that what he says can be taken as almost certain to happen. The Group is short of good Controllers. He himself has rejected thirty-two out of the thirty-five put up to him for training. Somewhat encouraged, Webland returns unenthusiastically to Cawford.

No one is positively unpleasant and yet there is this atmosphere not so much of unfriendliness as of non-comradeship, which is very palpable to one who has formerly breathed better air. It may be a congenital weakness of a Headquarters, where rank snobbery thrives and the weak or unlucky go under and putrefy.

There is a clothing parade, however, the following day, at which Webland is lucky, being permitted to exchange his nine-months-worn tunic and cap for new ones. Like a woman and her hat, the change is good for morale.

That evening, coming back to his billet at the far end of the camp, he meets some of his room-mates staggering under their blankets and kit-bags towards their new quarters in some oven-hot wooden huts. Experience has taught him the importance of not being the last to peg out a claim to a bed and, if possible, a lock-up box with a hasp to it. He has, of course, his own indispensable padlock. He manages to pack up and transport all his stuff in two journeys, with unexpected help from one of the younger airmen.

A wooden box is discovered in an unoccupied hut next door, and the bed he has chosen has two wooden shelves beside it, but only one nail to hang clothes on. Having had to manage in the past with no nail at all and no box, he is in luxury; and furthermore, he has secured a bed between two older and soberer men, one of whom, however, has the disturbing habit of grinding his teeth in his sleep.

On a journey between the huts he is overtaken by a voice which says: 'I thought it was you, Chiefie.' 'Chiefie' is new to him. He rather likes it. He also likes being called 'Squire' and 'Me old Chickadee'. Such names are a welcome change from the classy 'Old Boy', and the vulgar 'Oi, you', that Adam used to dread. The voice is that of the well-spoken young armourer, Tomkins, who had shared the ambulance to Stopfield and had not got scarlet fever. They have no time to do more than shake hands and wish one another 'All the best', but this cursory reunion after an acquaintance of less than a day gives him a disproportionate amount of pleasure.

Friendship is more to be missed than the money which he fails to receive at the pay parade next morning, held in cold rain, the men all wearing macintosh groundsheets. His name is not on the pay list, although he has been on the strength of Cawford for over six weeks. An Officer tells him to report at Pay Accounts the next morning: a bad time for a man on the night watch, who will only get to bed at 8 a.m. after early breakfast and will therefore have to rise again at 9. The inconvenience of time and place, however, is not the Officer's concern.

But that night the humane Corporal of No. 3 watch, knowing that Webland is supposed to get his deferred pay at 9, sends him off to bed at 3 a.m. Is it correct to say that Corporals are kinder than Sergeants, Sergeants than Flight Sergeants, and Flight Sergeants indisputably than Warrant Officers? Obviously not; yet it has often seemed so.

At Pay Accounts next morning he is turned away for not having a chit from the Orderly Room, although he had warily asked them yesterday if it was necessary to have one. Today is Saturday. They say: 'Come back with a chit at 1.30 on Monday.' It's lucky he's not totally dependent on his Service pay.

The cook-house food here is worse than at Bindover

or at Swanton. Not feeling like eating a stodgy lunch at
noon, he wanders into the Naffy where he notices buns
and cakes and tea. He orders some, but is informed that
none of this food is to be sold before 5.30, though he
can buy a cup of tea. Down on his luck today and
inclined to sulk, he retreats to the hut.

There are always tasks to be done at the bedside: sock
darning, button sewing, polishing. Today an hour and
more can be found for stitching the sparks of which no
one has yet tried to deprive him. The medal ribbon can
be fixed later. He is still a very slow seamster – if not a
sewer, which doesn't convey the right meaning in print.

The filthy talk goes on. Its purveyors are not in any
other way filthy themselves. Most of them are very agreeable and Webland likes almost all, and he thinks they
don't object to him. One of the clever younger ones –
and there are many good brains among these Ops airmen
– seeing Webland carrying a kit-bag for another airman
during the last hut move had called out cheerfully: 'Not
lost the old volunteer spirit yet, Webby?' Now this same
lad, slave to the paramount sexual expletive, calls out
across the hut in the general direction of Webland's
bed: 'Has anyone seen my (sexual) boots?' This is too
good to miss, so he replies: 'I don't know about the ones
you wear for that purpose, but these look as if they might
be yours.' The hut catches on very readily to the mis-
interpretation.

After but four days in occupation, all are ordered to
pack and be out of the hut forthwith. They are to move
back to a hut adjacent to the one before last that they
had occupied, far from the cook-house and the entrance
gates. It is said that the Waafs have been turned out of
their comparatively comfortable garden-house quarters to
make room for some Officers. They won't like coming
into Webland's hut, the washing and W.C. and general
amenities of which are distant, dirty and inadequate; so
no one is pleased.

Coming off duty at midnight he is persuaded to accompany some of the boys to the cook-house for supper, which is as unappetizing as usual. There he finds once more the disgraced ex-Sergeant Daly. Perhaps he also is lonely at Cawford, finding no punch-drunk soul mates. He wants Webland to go and watch him fight in an all-in wrestling match next month against some champion, and he will give him a ticket. Such an honour has not come Webland's way before, and he is torn between the wish not to hurt the fighter's feelings and a disinclination to witness the spectacle. Can such a fighter's command be disregarded? His imminent posting will probably settle the matter for him.

Daly says he doesn't like calling him Webland. What is his first name? So it is Arthur and Mick henceforward, if there be any common henceforward, which seems un-likely.

Monday does bring Webland's pay, £3–5–0, and not without effort, thus: collect an officer's signed chit from the Orderly Room; take it to Pay Accounts by 1.15 p.m.; return at 2; wait half an hour, sign an album, then receive the cash.

After tea, to their fourth billet within three weeks, Webland and his mates move their belongings. It is full summer and very hot under the loads of kit-bags, coats, blankets and pillows. There is a rumour that their stay here will not be long either. The baths are across a path some thirty yards distant from the hut, the wash basins sixty yards, and the W.C. about thirty in another direction. This hut is of stone, has sixty beds and will be cooler under the sun than the last one.

The frequent fifty-six hours off and visits to London have helped to colour an otherwise dull period. Now, a month after his last visit home, he gets another seven days' leave, from which in three days' time he is recalled to Cawford for the expected posting. The only regret at all will be the loss of Vera. There is no time to say good-bye, only to scribble a note to her before bedtime. The next morning, which is Midsummer Day, will be taken

up with packing and getting himself elaborately signed
out of this impersonal establishment. He should report at
Overhill aerodrome at about tea-time; and high time, too,
since this marks the final step on the way to his commission.

9

Not Wanted

Iago: Why, there's no remedy; 'tis the curse of
service,
Preferment goes by letter and affection.
SHAKESPEARE – *Othello*

In blazing sunshine Webland pursues the complications
of moving from one camp to another fifteen miles away,
this time, though, with few regrets. Vera says that it is
much friendlier at a Sector and that he's bound to be
an Officer very soon now. Her parting gift is the green
pillow-slip.

Breakfast then, at seven, packing his gear, and off
round the camp with his Clearance Chit to be signed at
over a dozen points. That takes from 8.30 until 10.30,
when, with many an 'All the best!' from Orderly Room,
Flight Sergeant and others, laden with kit-bag, handbag,
haversack and respirator, he arrives sweating at the bus
stop outside the gates. The bus conductress, perhaps
through pity at his damp and panting appearance, refuses
to let him pay the fare to the station. So far so friendly.
Now for presentation to the fresh life and comrades.

The first figure met outside Overhill aerodrome is
foreign. He looks like an Officer. Let him have the
honour of a good English salute. Down with the baggage,
out of the mouth with the pipe, change a new blue
enamel mug from right hand to left, and up with a smart
right hand to the bonnet. An American smile lights

up the world: 'Seems an awful lot of trouble for so liddle.'

He finds his way to a twelve-bedded Nissen hut where he is to sleep: a hut for new arrivals, with blankets and biscuits to each bed, but no bolster or pillow to fill Vera's pillow-slip. A tough-looking but not inimical lad from Glasgow puts him on the road to the cook-house, half an hour's walk away.

There the food is good: help yourself to spam, meat pie, new bread, margarine, jam and tea, in the company of many blond Norwegians. So far everyone has been most friendly, just as Vera had said, including the Orderly Room L.A.C. and the S.P. at the Guard Room: a new experience. Never was a first night in Webland's long service like this. Almost cheerfully he arranges his blankets for entry and looks forward to more courtesies tomorrow.

Reporting to the Orderly Room at nine, he is sent to Pay Accounts a few yards away, where they do nothing for him. Back again to have his twelve-fifty altered from Cawford to Overhill and be instructed to make his way to an expropriated country house called Thorn Grove, a few miles down the road, they say. There should be a bus at about twenty-past ten. Anxious to know who pays for the bus ride, he is told that if he keeps the bus ticket and puts in a seventeen-seventy-one to Pay Accounts he might get the money.

Anxious also to find out about the chances of getting his interrupted leave continued, he learns that he will have to wait for Records to come through. Well, Records at Swanton have been known to come through seven months after a man has been posted elsewhere. Overhill is in no hurry; nor are Records; nor in fact is Webland.

Realizing that, when he gets to Thorn Grove, he may find that there is nowhere for him to sleep and that he may be ordered to bring all his things back again to Overhill this afternoon, he sits on his kit-bag in the gutter outside the aerodrome gates in the sunshine waiting for eastbound transport in the direction of Stenge village. The Glasgow lad, passing by, says:

'Don't get pinched by the Warrant Officer, sitting on your kit-bag. He'll say it's not airmanlike and be vairy angry.'

An army lorry stops, the driver's mate jumps down, heaves his kit-bag into the back, and he is transported to the lodge gates of Thorn Grove. Five minutes' walk up the drive and he reports to a Flight Sergeant who says they have been expecting him. This is so unexpected as to be almost sinister. The C.O., says the Flight Sergeant, wants to see Webland, but he's not there at the moment. When, however, the C.O. who is called Squadron Leader Spruce-Jones returns, he doesn't want to see him.

He stands about until one o'clock when a motor coach takes him and other airmen a mile or so to a meal at Low's Barn, where their mess and cook-house are. Having eaten, he is conducted, still with kit-bag on shoulders bruised from yesterday's carrying, on a quarter of an hour's march to Grey Cottage, Stenge, where he is put in a garret at the top of the building. In the garret are three iron and wire bedsteads, mostly in pieces, a coil of fire-escape rope, no electric bulb, seven wall pegs, a small high shelf, and a dormer window overlooking a garden.

This looks a right abode for an unsociable elderly airman who has shared a hut with upwards of forty men for the last three and a half months: provided, that is, no one comes to share it with him. Vain thought. Such privacy cannot last more than a few nights, at most. Pray, then, for peaceable companions. Goodness knows how many men crowd this little house; perhaps twenty-five or thirty: soldiers too, he observes. There will be many fatigues, such as washing and polishing floors and furniture, gardening, firewatching, and probably sentry duty as well.

The big house at Thorn Grove, lived in before the war

by friends of his, is now, with its outhouses and grounds, serving as an Operations station. There Webland is to be trained for this shadowy commission as Ops B.

There is commendably little delay in his initiation, for he is to start work with 'A' watch tonight at eight o'clock until midnight. There is to be no getting outside camp between watches. So much the better if it means progress. Now that they know about him and what he is bound for there should be no more frustrations, re-musterings and wrong papers.

With three damp biscuits and one damp blanket airing in the window, three more blankets to be fetched from the mess at Low's Barn, Webland has reason to be fairly well satisfied with the day's achievement. He reports for his first spell of duty that night.

As at Cawford, the skill here is with maps and telephones, keeping communication with pilots going and coming between earth and sky by night and day. A Corporal spends most of his time instructing Webland. This seems a much friendlier place than Cawford. It is smaller, of course, and none of his colleagues yet knows anything of his connexions or what he is there for, or in what way, if any, his situation differs from that of the others.

The scales soon fall from his eyes. The next night's watch is more than twice as long as that of the first one: from midnight to eight-thirty; and most of it is spent standing or sweeping, wiping and carrying buckets of clean and dirty hot water. Here there are no General Duties lads, as at Cawford, to char for the airmen of the watch. There is a rest-room where a man may lie down for a restless hour or two; but it seems to Webland already that learning is likely to take second place to fatigues.

And where is the *esprit de corps*? Obviously at the aerodrome among the crews, for it is not down here at Thorn Grove. A day and a half of seeing and hearing has revealed that much, and it is in the fatigues that it is most apparent. The airmen are, in fact, dispirited. Almost all are young aspirants who, as in the case of those in the Ops Room at Cawford, have been grounded and sent away from their beloved flying courses.

From snatches of talk with these ex-angels Webland begins to understand how the acid of their new earth-life has eaten into their souls, and he soon ceases to find their company as distasteful as he did at first.

Fifty-six hours' leave has been granted him on Thursday, only a week since his arrival. That means two nights at home to make up for the missing four. There's more waiting, more patience: twenty-five minutes in a telephone kiosk to let his wife know this good news; but futile: can't get through. There's plenty of time though, for it's only Monday.

The duties take their daily and nightly round. There is very little Ops work or instruction, much sitting about. He is getting the impression, hinted to him by a sympathetic comrade, that he is being used as an odd boy to relieve and fatigue and generally do anything convenient, which may not be helpful to his training but may be useful to the cynical-eyed Sergeant of the watch and his friends.

By degrees he finds himself set at the door of the Ops Room as a sort of janitor, and this is growing to be his particular post, even as at Swanton Adam had found himself mail carrier and Webland bicycle cleaner-in-chief to the Flight Sergeant. Since he has not been at Overhill long enough to recognize inhabitants or visitors he lets them all pass into the room, hoping he won't get into trouble for letting through a spy. When an Officer comes by he stands up, then resumes his seat and his book or his letter writing.

On a list of names he reads that he is to firewatch during the next night and act odd-man at Grey Cottage during the day. He does not mind this except that it means not spending all possible time near or inside the Ops Room and so adding to his knowledge against the day of test. There is said to be a school of instruction somewhere for airmen like him, but the Flight Sergeant in charge cannot tell him when he is to be sent there. He just says: 'Oh, you'll be going there sure enough.' This might have encouraged Webland had he not then discovered that his laundry has not been forwarded from Cawford and is likely to be lost for ever. Such a mis-adventure crowds out all other thoughts.

Heart-break stories are even more common here than at Swanton. A Signals L.A.C. spends a quarter of an hour leaning over Webland's table at the door of the Ops Room, reciting the sorry way in which he has been treated. Is it so common, then, this injustice and dis-content, or is it just Webland's fate to get thrown among and be the confidant of fallen men? This is the reason why these lads of the watches are such unedifying com-panions, weighed down themselves and weighing Web-land down with their grumbles, so that each day he has to heave his spirits up as out of a bog.

The fifty-six hours' leave comes, therefore, as a much needed tonic; and a letter from Vera at Cawford tells him that several of his colleagues there still miss him and say how different he was and what wonderful ideas he had. Wonderful ideas? That's a bit of extra, inspired by Vera's well-known tendency to flatter. Yet will the C.O. at Overhill think his ideas wonderful enough to merit a commission?

Returned from leave, Webland is surprised to be allowed to sit on the dais in the Ops Room among the Controllers. Soon tired of staring at the uncommunicative map far below and trying to listen to other people's instructions, he finds beside him an album of orders to do with aircraft and operations. Seeing a chance of learning something, he takes the precaution of asking a young Officer for leave to look at the album, and obtains it. This Officer had been a Corporal at Cawford and was a living proof that a commission can be won from an Ops Room.

A profitable half hour is spent, for the book contains just the sort of information to help a future Ops B Officer. The only thing marring the half hour is the leaning over and hot breathing upon him by an airman who thinks he will share the reading. A prod in the back turns Webland round. There stands the Sergeant of the watch, he of the cynical eye, an ex-commercial traveller named Hayward, capable and self-confident.

'Who gave you permission to look at that book?'

'Flying Officer Armitage, Sergeant.'

'Well, I'm not allowed to look at it, but if Mr Armitage says you can, then you can.'

This is an unwanted victory producing an uncomfortable situation. Webland can only think of easing it, with the hot-breathing airman leering behind, by mumbling: 'No; if you mayn't, I shan't read it either.'

What will proud Hayward think of this? He eyes Webland like a man determined to solve some puzzle, wholly challenging and half amused.

Two airmen are said to have been posted suddenly. Webland is therefore relieved of fatigue duty at Grey Cottage and is ordered to do night sentry go at Thorn Grove. He hasn't sentry gone since that moonlight night at Cadstone last September, and, although this again means missing valuable hours of possible instruction in Ops, he will be glad to have a rifle and bayonet in his hands once more. It will also make a change from feeling superfluous as a dummy janitor or contemplating a floor-scrubber's knee-high point of view.

With A/Cs Frisk and Watson, steel hats, groundsheets and ceremonial grey webbing belts, Webland reports to the Guard Room at 5 p.m., to do two hours on and four hours off throughout the night, for a week of guardsmanship. He feels a stouter man already, especially when the Guard Room Corporal, an ex-Sergeant of the Black Watch in the last war, who remembers General Victor Fortune joining the regiment at Perth over thirty years ago, remarks on the difference with which Webland handles his rifle from the general run of airmen. His dormant pride stirs again.

The July weather is still fairly good and not too hot. Each night imitates the one before; each day sleep refreshes in the garret at Grey Cottage. On duty from 5.30 p.m. until 6 a.m.; then breakfast and bed; then up and tea; and on again. On duty there is an outhouse to lie down in, between spells of sentry-go, in clothes and boots on an unclean bed, while four other unprofessional members of the guard lounge, talking and smoking, all ready to turn out in thirty theoretical seconds. The Corporal gives them all half an hour's arms drill, with an Angus and Forfar accent, rich and husky, before posting them on guard.

Frisk and Watson, who must have been debating the question, ask Webland if he is any relation to Montagu Webland. They say 'Go on!' when he admits it. 'No joking?' They cannot believe it and want to know what on earth made him join the ranks. Always pleasant to him, they are even more so now.

In the morning comes a letter from Frank written from his neighbouring aerodrome. Having heard that Webland is at Overhill he has telephoned to Spruce-Jones, the yet uninterviewed-by C.O. at Thorn Grove, to say for God's sake look after A/C Webland. He hears that Vera is to be posted to Overhill and has asked that she shall be put on the same watch as Webland. 'Telephone to me,' he continues, 'if you want anything; I can fix things with Spruce.' Dear old Frank. Can things really be so fixed? What should Webland ask for but his illusory commission which it seems in no one's power to offer?

He gets a different sentry mate on guard each night. As in the old song: 'On Monday I walked out with a soldier; on Tuesday I walked out with a tar', on Monday he did sentry with a Coventry pawnbroker; on Tuesday with a Liverpool school attendance officer; on Wednesday with an Islington cabinetmaker who threw over the Roman Catholic religion when the Pope backed General Franco against the Spanish Government.

Whenever cars come to Thorn Grove the sentry has to stop them and be shown a pass. On Friday morning a car slows down as it approaches Webland with his rifle and bayonet, but when he is about to ask the driver for his pass, the high-ranking Officer in the back calls out testily: 'Drive on!' Webland jumps out of the way. Now what is he to do? He has a bullet in his rifle. He cannot be certain of firing straight enough to puncture a tyre. His mind races forward in alarm. Ought he to shoot? If he does not he is guilty of dereliction of duty. Dereliction is a hard sounding word. What does it really mean? Suppose he shoots and the bullet bounces off the road into the spine of the Officer in the car; or into the breast of a passing Waaf? At the Court Martial they will say: 'Didn't it ever occur to you to use a little common sense, airman?'

But suppose the Officer in the car is a German with a bomb in his brief-case and in half an hour Ops goes sky high? Oh well, it's too late now.

When Webland and his mate, a divorced carpenter from the mouth of the Thames, report the matter to the Corporal of the Guard, he only laughs. What are the rights and wrongs of this? That Officers should play the game by sentries? Webland must remember when he becomes a swell always to be kind to sentries. To add a further anxiety, that night the relieving sentries are ten minutes late at the 2 a.m. turn. To Webland it seems unpardonable to be late for such a tryst, especially as it is raining.

Sentry week comes to an end, to be succeeded next day by firewatching, which is mostly sleeping. After the firewatching comes, naturally enough in a play upon words, charring. At Low's Barn his job is to sweep the passages and stairs, then mop them with hot water and disinfectant. All baths and basins are cleaned with brown powder. An interesting detail with an element of treasure hunting is the picking up of cigarette ends from the paths and soil beneath the men's windows. All this, with a mate, takes no more than two hours in the morning. The rest, until the 8 p.m. watch, is leisure.

Webland is pleased by a letter from Peter Bagshaw, an old school friend and most unsuitable temporary soldier, who has been for a year an Ensign in the Brigade of Guards. At Pirbright, he says, he gets printed bits of paper from London, signed by one of the younger boys in their house at school who is a Lieutenant-Colonel in the regiment. Peter is sardonically comforting:

'I am sorry about your getting stuck. I think the R.A.F. is all run by influence, even more than the Army. So you should get your father to write to the S/S for Air whoever he is and you would get a commission in a fortnight. As you probably won't do that you had better get transferred into the Army, more particularly into this regiment, and anyhow it's much more fun.

'Mark tried to get a commission in the Air Force in some humble administrative capacity and was accepted by them and then they decided they didn't want him because they were going to give all that kind of job to pilots who had bombed Berlin thirty times and needed a rest. So they may have changed their mind about you for the same reason. Now Mark is a rifleman, and if he isn't very idle he should get a commission soon.'

Gossip with airmen on the watch reveals that there is little to be learnt at Thorn Grove. The instruction school is the target to aim at, but that is now closed and will not re-open before the week after next when its Sergeant returns from leave; and then Webland may not be chosen to go to it. He has borrowed a book on navigation and meteorology which he proposes to master in the meantime.

The next day comes a blessed 56-hour pass, and home. The best sight on returning to Overhill is Vera on the midnight watch. There is plenty of time for talking, activity on the map being slight. The eight hours' duty goes by normally, with watching and gossiping for two and a half hours, scrubbing and cleaning the premises and making the young Squadron Leader's bed for an hour and a half, sleeping for three hours, and watching again for the final hour. Four weeks of this have been accomplished. As a course of instruction it does seem deficient and without system.

Two solaces are the occasional talks and laughs with Vera and the fact that he is still the sole occupant of the garret at Grey Cottage. When that privacy ends it will be without warning, so he keeps his nerves ready for an intrusion at any time. A minor worry is his long lost laundry and he gets permission one day to go to Cawford to try and trace it. This outing begins with a sprint from Low's Barn, lunchless, to catch a 1.19 train a quarter of a mile away at Stenge station. From London he starts again for Cawford. There the Guard Room requires explanation and persuasion before admitting him to the camp. The Orderly Room is helpful although the laundry Corporal is away visiting the dentist, so the time is passed in queueing up for tea at the cook-house. Later it is discovered from a record that his laundry was sent to Overhill three weeks ago. He then walks two miles to a Group Captain's house to fetch a tennis racquet that Vera had left there and delivers it to the flat of one of her friends in London. Then back to camp to find no news of the three weeks' laundry, last week's laundry containing another man's villainous socks instead of his own home-made ones, and the attic room in total disarray, beds outside, blankets on the roof, pyjamas hidden: said to be the effect of a jovial raid on 'A' watch by the watches 'C' and 'D'. This will probably lead to reprisal and then what peace can ever be?

The following night he lies long awake in the rest-room in the dark, half undressed, beside four sleeping airmen, wondering whether he would do well to try a change, as Mark had done, into the Army. It is nearly eleven months now since he was called up, and by applying and being accepted for a commission and doing nothing more to further it than strive to do his tasks and to obey orders, he has got nowhere, and slowly.

He has not been spoken to yet by his Commanding Officer, in spite of Frank's assurance that he would see that all went well for him. A few days ago when he was on his knees scrubbing a corridor, the C.O. had seemed to look at him in half-recognition, but then had stepped over him and passed on. Perhaps he is absent-minded. Or he may be browned off, so that, as taints spread downwards through organizations, some of the brown has come off on his juniors right down to the bottom.

Suddenly – everything has to happen suddenly and after hopes or fears have long withered with waiting – the very next day he is told to report at the school of instruction in Stenge with seven fresh-posted Waafs as fellow pupils, under a male Corporal teacher.

The Corporal knows that Webland has long since mastered all his elementary teaching, so he allows him to sit in a chair apart and read or write as he pleases. He is also a bit annoyed that an airman who has already spent over two months in Ops Rooms has been sent to him with these female novices.

Listening to the lesson, Webland is cheered to realize how much of the work he knows already. Total ignorance must have been assumed for him to be sent to this elementary place of instruction; or is there a darker reason?

Only by chance is he able to make a little progress on the second day, because the seven Waafs, on behalf of whom this course has been laid out, have been summoned to a Pay Parade and will not appear until the afternoon. He looks forward to some private and more advanced tuition from Corporal West. But the Corporal overslept that morning and has not arrived even by ten o'clock; so his pupil sits outside in the early sunshine studying his book on navigation. The Corporal turns up in time for an hour and a half's teaching of the sort of things Webland wants to know.

But that is all the good that has come of this much-looked-forward-to course, for his seven days' leave is now due and he appears, so far as any more instruction is concerned, to have, as they say, had it.

On his return from leave, he learns that several of the men have been posted overseas: a fate dreaded like death. Despite the spirit of solipsism that hangs about Thorn Grove, his comrades appear glad to see him back again, perhaps because he can accompany their lusty songs on the Low's Barn piano. The routine of Ops and fatigue is taken up once more: headphones and plotting on the map, minding the door, polishing linoleum and scrubbing stone. A passer-by asks Webland's fatigue mate what the two of them are washing the front porch for. Glumly McWilliam replies: 'The King of Switzerland.'

One night soon afterwards, while Webland is idly talking to Vera in the Ops Room, a reputedly rather incompetent Officer asks him if he can show him anything or answer any questions. There follows a useful lesson on the subject of Ops B's duties which fills up a quiet half-hour. Most of the rest of the time he spends, of course, as door sentry. A verse from the Psalms comes to his mind: 'I had rather be a door-keeper in the house of my God than to dwell in the tents of ungodliness'; but in this case the alternatives are not applicable.

Even Frank now suspects that Webland has slipped down some administrative pot-hole and that only something of a Stygian future can be expected for him here. Has he heard something that he can't pass on? The suspicion is confirmed by Vera who has learnt in two- three- and four-ringed circles of the Air Force that there can be no commission for Webland, in Fighter Command at any rate. But why should they bother to say such a thing, even if they are aware of his fatiguing existence? Perhaps Vera should not have told him this. He is not sure whether he is glad or not; whether even to believe it.

On returning to Grey Cottage the next evening he is shocked to find his garret occupied by two guests unpacking and assembling their beds. There is only one thing to be done and that is to give them as good an imitation of a genuine welcome as he can, make room for them to hang things on the pegs, and study how to make the best of their unwanted company.

These two young strangers are both unhappy because, for medical reasons, they have been removed from aircrew training and have been posted on and on while never losing all hope that they may get back into the air again. Not too brutally Webland hints to them that, having at last arrived at Thorn Grove, they might now abandon all hope of soon becoming the Deputy Controllers that they've been told they should. He discloses to them the atmosphere of the Ops Room, where, if an airman by grumbling or wheedling gets a small job of importance to do, he incurs the envy of the others, who cannot rest until they get him back on to doing fatigues once more. It is like living in a poultry run, where peck, snatch, run and hide controls all operations from the highest to the lowest rank. It has to be experienced to be understood.

Bertie Barrett and Len Moore understand pretty well, for they have been in the pit of degradation long enough to recognize the dark shapes that inhabit it.

Bertie, who is the younger, comes from the west where his father is a Coastguard. He has been training for aircrew for about a year in the American continent. He is fair, blue-eyed, vivacious and combative-looking, although of no great physique. He speaks with a slight Canadian veneer upon a natural Devon accent.

Len was born in Canada, but was brought up in the county of his fathers at Preston, where he keeps a shop. He also has had copious training as an air-pilot. He is dark, almost to gipsyness, and, though not tall, is very powerfully built. He speaks with a slight Lancashire accent in which is no trace of his Canadian birth.

Good young men they may be, or bad, or neither; Webland's life at Thorn Grove can never be the same henceforward, with two such vivid personalities to sleep and wake beside in this small room. The newcomers have grave doubts about this middle-aged, toffish air-craftman, who, before getting into bed, seems to think he's a clergyman. Such goings-on trouble Bertie, so that he mutters to his companion:

'We've got a right one here, Len, and no mistake.'

Len is not talkative. He is a student of his fellow men. 'Wait and see.'

Len, by virtue of his strength of body and character, as well as his few years' seniority, is evidently the dominant partner in the friendship, though Bertie keeps his end up and never gives in. Webland hopes he can somehow become accepted by these two, if only as a not objectionable third party. He likes them already and is very willing to do more than his share with them in the garret and outside.

On arriving at the garret at seven o'clock next evening to clean up and set his bed in shape for the night, there are his two new room-mates with a warm 'Hello, Webby', and his own bed made, better than he'd ever made it himself.

'Who's done this glorious thing for me?'

Len's glance indicates Bertie. Bertie looks comically proud. Everything is going to be all right with chaps like these. They talk late and discover unsuspected sympathies, including the fact that Webland too has visited Canada nearly twenty years ago.

Business at the aerodrome next morning brings Webland into communication with the Flight Lieutenant Admin., who seems interested enough to ask him about his occupation at Thorn Grove. He suggests that he ought to do something about this commission, but doesn't really know what. 'It's no good just waiting,' he says, 'or you'll never get anywhere.' Just in time to see the bus to Stenge diminish down the road, Webland waits not but walks the four miles back to the billet.

Vera has been successfully flannelling the Flight Sergeant to give her a leave pass and let her off the night watch. She has also procured similar latitude from the Squadron Leader. Everyone likes helping Vera who repays them by her gay originality. While she makes her preparations, Webland is sent hot from his trudge to dig in some vegetable allotments, which job, thanks to his physical fitness, is easily dealt with. Even missing a spell in the Ops Room doesn't upset him now, and there is little to choose in pleasure between minding the door in the fug and spading in the August heat outside.

'You know, you're a dry beggar, Webby,' says Len, sparing of words as of flattery, after some quip of Webland's. Len has the measure of everyone already, the flannellers, the twisters, the boasters, the hollow and the sound. He is much amused by Waaf talk and accent: 'Perfectly bladdy, ectually', he says they say.

Oddly enough, the women don't display any jealousy over who does what in the Ops Room, probably because they don't have to scrub and door-keep elsewhere than in their own quarters. As for Webland, he thinks that he has obtained as much skill as most of the others at plotting, and further skill at that would be no use to him as an Officer; so he is not in the competition. In any case he is now practically a professional janitor; so much so that no one is envious of him and one or two have remarked that the N.C.O.s, particularly Sergeant Hayward and his subordinate Sergeants, take pleasure in humiliating A/C Webland, whose impassiveness under stress they deem quite singular. As a matter of fact he feels no humiliation. He is simply perplexed.

In their hours of leisure, while he lies on his bed reading a book, or is cleaning his boots and buttons, Len and Bertie, like tireless puppies, chaff each other in light or heavy vein. Webland likes them too well to mind the noise and gets in now and then with what Len would call a dry remark. Sometimes when they are more disposed for peace, Bertie writes to his parents or his girl friends, while Len sings pianissimo in a melodious baritone.

The weather at the end of August has been getting hotter and more airless, and a sweating sleep is hard to secure in the little room close under the roof. Then at last comes the rain, in torrents.

There have been American soldiers at a camp near Stenge for the past few weeks, and Webland has enjoyed being nodded to in the village, with a half-wave of the hand and a word that sounds like 'Howyer'. There seems no friction with the British.

On this tempestuous night the street is peopled by lost, belated, slightly tipsy but good-tempered Americans, hollering to one another through the streaming darkness and trying to find their ways five miles back to their camp. They imagine, poor fellows, that if only they can be directed to the police station there will appear a tutelary truck to bear them home. Knowing our own lack of transport, our airmen think these visitors fancy themselves in a pre-war world of plenty; but sure enough, a little farther on, as Webland and his mates are sloshing along the water-logged gutter, there is an army truck calling and calling again for lost American soldiers.

Earlier in the evening, before the rain, he had accompanied for the first time one of the Sergeants and three airmen to a pub round the corner. All felt dry before the storm, and, as Webland drank, they watched him narrowly. To have partaken of what they call in these parts a half-skeyner proved that he was as good a fellow as they had hoped, and their delight was perceptible. He had to explain that when he was not thirsty he did not drink, but when he was, then he did drink. This ridiculous reasoning made them smile and strengthened their opinion that he was a very queer fish.

It is the 6th September. A year ago this day he had left home to achieve, if not glory, at least some semblance

o

of being useful. The uniform he wears has not sniffed the smoke of battle, nor has any foreign missile broken its surface. It has been twice fumigated and once cleaned where oily bicycles of Sergeants have rubbed against it; it has also once been invisibly mended when acid from a battery was spilt upon it. So far as he can recall not a drum beat has helped to shorten the miles of road he has marched, as often as not alone. In the current R.A.F. jargon, what has it all been in aid of?

This anniversary should be a night of celebration. Well, he has drunk half a skeyner with an N.C.O., and that's about the worth of a year's effort. So much for the first; here's to the second. Tomorrow he goes on another seven days' leave.

The leave days at home race by as they always do, and on the day before returning to Overhill Webland walks the mile and a half across the fields to say good-bye to his parents at Amberdine. He pauses at the edge of the garden and climbs the steps of the gazebo for a look at the old house. Here where he stands was the Headquarters of Roland's K.R.A. All about the grounds they used to hold their manoeuvres, stalking and skirmishing, through the rock garden and the orchard and the yew-walk and the nut-walk and the kitchen and the walled gardens. On the left is the cedar tree in which Roland had been judged shot on night operations and had characteristically refused to admit it. Like a true Briton he never knew when he was beaten. And there, above the theatre-room where they had staged so many plays, was the clock tower with its bell in silhouette against the northern sky. The distance is fully a hundred yards and he remembers his satisfaction when as a schoolboy he had knelt one evening where he stands now, with his rifle beaded on that bell, waiting for the hammer to make the last stroke of seven o'clock. His bullet had sped true and had hit the bell at exactly the right moment to make it eight. He hadn't considered the danger of a ricochet, but only how worried his friend Beeston the butler would be, thinking

it must be dinner-time already and him not yet changed
into his evening serving clothes.

What a world of servants it was in those days; and one
took them all for granted: the gardeners, the men-
servants and the maidservants, all ministering to the
handful of patricians that formed the family. Was it
right? Was it wrong? It was certainly happy, as many
have since averred, on both sides of the social fence, for
all except an odd one or two. His sister, Lucretia, was
one of the odd ones; whereas old Betty, who had retired
after forty years of fatigues as a housemaid, never ceased
blessing the good old days at Amberdine. Perhaps one
day a senile Webland would be heard extolling the care-
free life of a mis-posted airman.

But all that, or the best of it, had ended with the First
World War, and after it things were never quite the same.
There was less of quiet Amberdine and more of official
residences with press and public never far away, policemen in attendance, and, as in *The Gondoliers* song, holders
of high office, as 'cheap as sprats' and 'plentiful as tabby-
cats', until the whole array of dignitaries became no
more than figures in a magic toyshop seeking prominent
places on higher shelves. Familiarity had performed its
dismal task of disenchantment. But it was never so with
Amberdine . . .

Come, Theodore, you must get along to the house
and give the old people an account of your doings.

10
Not Suited

Plus ne suis ce que j'ai été,
Et plus ne saurais jamais l'être;
Mon beau printemps et mon été
Ont fait le saut par la fenêtre.
CLÉMONT MAROT – *Chanson*

It must be supposed that the authorities have learnt by
generations of experience how much leave is healthy for
servicemen. At Cawford and at Overhill airmen can get
away from the camp for hours or days so often that the
neighbours at home, whose boys are perhaps serving
overseas, are not far from turning nasty when they
observe young Smith or Brown home again for the third
time this month. 'Don't they ever do any work at all in
the Raff? My boy hasn't been home since Christmas,
except for that couple of days at Easter.'

On the other hand where the work is concentrated, as
at Cadstone and Bindover, the men's minds are on the
job, morale is good, and they have no time to be wondering why they can't be sent home instead of mucking
about here doing what the troops call sweet fanny adams.
In fact, if at places with a spirit of disservice the lads
were not sent home at frequent intervals, their belly-
aching might boil up into an ulcerous situation that the
authorities would find difficult to treat. Hence the inverse
justice of the hard-working getting few leave passes and
the scroungers getting plenty.

Len and Bertie, after many hopes and successes in their war career, have now arrived, through no fault of their own, at the lowest point of their fortunes. They are ranked as L.A.C.s, and their recent reverses have bred in them a determination to be made suckers of no longer. Henceforward the R.A.F. is to be the sucker. This is a game, in which they may score some marks now and then, but it is one that they are unlikely to win.

To them, fortunately for him, Webland does not represent the Service. He is obviously a fellow victim, and as such, as soon as he has shown his willingness to take his share in the duller duties of their station, he is made to feel that he has their close support. They judge, for instance, that he is a duffer in domestic matters. Seeing him fumbling with a needle at a button or peering for dust about his bed space, one of them will say with mock gruffness:

'Come on now, Webby, move yourself. You get on your bunk and I'll soon fix it.'

There is little that he can do for them in kind but, if ever they want to get off for a few hours, he is ready to take their place on duty, to make their beds and prepare some sort of a welcome for their return. Liquor and its effects are fortunately not a problem among the three garreteers, and for that Webland is grateful. Vomiting and violence, which are common features of wartime service life, he might have found hard to put up with. Swearing, blasphemy and foul jokes leave him unconcerned; but there is little of that here.

At the Ops Room Sergeant Hayward is away for three weeks and Sergeant Wooller is in charge. By way of tightening up discipline Wooller has ordained that in future any airman or Waaf loitering about the doorway and gossiping will be put on a charge. Since Webland is more often door sentry than anyone else, this is going to take away some of the social pleasantries which help to pass the tour of duty. But it will mean less interruption of his reading and writing.

Len believes that this rule, whether on instruction from the C.O. or not, has been made particularly to oppress Webland. He says he has already noticed the animosity of Sergeant James – 'Jimmy' or 'the miniature Neanderthal' – which results in the choice of Webland for all the dirty jobs. 'Even Sergeant Hayward,' says Len, 'who is intelligent enough to know better, delights in his power to attempt Webby's humiliation; but the old poker-face and infinite patience annoy and defeat them all the time.'

Webland is scarcely conscious of this, but to Len it is all clearly part of the war within the war: the war between the lowly and the mighty.

Even Vera seems to be affected by the dark genius of the place. Not that she is ever disagreeable; but her moods swing from very gay to rather glum. Yesterday she was enchanting the coach-load on the way to lunch, making Waafs, airmen and N.C.O.s gleeful, enlivening them all with mercurial changes of expression, crooning '*Dear* little Boojums' and other such fond words to fascinated Waaf comrades. Today she is low-spirited. She may be upset about the new arrangement in the Ops Room whereby everyone is to take a turn at the various jobs; in fact, there is to be almost a system. Sergeant Wooller is responsible for this. He is impervious to Vera's flannellings and yesterday deposed her brusquely. No one can understand this, for everyone knows that Vera flourishes in the sunshine of the young Squadron Leader's favour and that Webland, who still has had no word from him, does not. It is not Vera's fault that because of the C.O. she enjoys preferment, but she is evidently displeased, and sits reading a detective story.

More strange still, Sergeant Wooller, who, whether he knows it or not, must surely be skating fast on thinnish ice, yesterday interrogated Webland. He asked how long he had been at Thorn Grove and what work he had done in Ops. When he learnt that he had been there three months and had had little opportunity of being taught anything valuable, he said it was a bloody poor show,

that the watch had been run on favouritism, and that so
long as he was in charge Webland was to be freed from
stooge watch duties and was to sit up on the dais and
learn all he could. Suspicion and intrigue are everywhere,
and Webland cannot think of an oblique enough cause
for this indulgence. Can it be an inter-Sergeant feud?

Fifty-six hours of leave interrupt the new learning
under Sergeant Wooller. He must learn all he can while
Sergeant Hayward is away. On his return he finds two
letters on his bed, neatly made for him as always by
one of the garret lads, for whom he has come to feel a
warm friendliness; so much so that he would protest if
he were told he was to have the garret to himself once
more.

One letter is from Skelding, of Cadstone and Swanton,
with whom he had been posted on the radio course to
Bindover. He is operating in North Wales at the trade
for which they had both been so carefully trained, and
to which the sparks on Webland's sleeve still bear now
pointless testimony. He says that two of the more
plausible of their old recruit colleagues are now Acting
Pilot Officers. 'Simply bloody amazing,' he adds.

The other letter is from Adam, at last established as
the bandsman he should have been from the start. Both
have similar tales to tell of delays and mispostings,
neglect and intrigue. With his usual farcical luck Adam's
transference has been gummed up for weeks by an
official failure to read the records right. The mistake in
the understanding of his true qualifications was only
discovered by chance, when he found himself sent for
by an Officer to help with some digging to do with a
bomb shelter. It had been observed in his file at Headquarters that his name had been entered as a former
Mineral Director, though whether this had to do with
mining or with aerated waters was not made clear.
Adam, puzzled at having been sent for, protested that he
was merely a musician. They told him he was not. Then
one Officer, brighter than his fellows, studied the record

again and saw that someone had misread musical as mineral. 'Bloody bad handwriting,' they grumbled.

Instead of the expected three weeks of Sergeant Wooller's rule, after one week only his watch duties are to cease, and Sergeant Hayward, recalled from his course, is to return. The old ways will return with him. Webland has had a more informative few days in the Ops Room than in all the four months since he was first posted to Operations. Sergeant Wooller says that Webland hasn't had a fair chance and doesn't see how he can be expected to make the grade, whatever it is, whenever it comes. Vera, on the other hand, has regained her high spirits, after uncorking her grievance to Wooller, demanding an interview with Spruce-Jones, and causing herself to be reinstated on high-class work once more. Having fought for her rights with the same vigour that she recommends for Webland, regardless of N.C.O.s and colleagues alike, she will prosper once more under the fell Sergeant's rule, and Webland will surely not.

So the idling days go by, when one evening Sergeant James, finding Webland alone in the rest-room, sits down beside him for a chat. He seems to have something on his mind, though there may not be very much room for it. Consequently they talk about nothing in particular. Just before leaving, Jimmy says:

'You'd 'a' done better to've stopped in the factory, the way you've been mucked about.'

From his manner of saying this Webland gets the impression, only the very faintest, though, that someone wants him to be posted overseas as a second-class airman at the earliest moment. It is no more than an admonitory instinct, an early warning of danger; and it seems to him that the little Sergeant, his supposed enemy, looks as if he knows something more than he dares say. Webland would find Thorn Grove a most sinister place if he had any serious fears for his future, but he has not. Overseas holds none of the terrors for him that it seems to hold for some of his colleagues.

Told of the incident that evening, Len, who has a wider knowledge of these things, doesn't like the sound of it at all. Nor does Bertie. Webland's report of his suspicions sets Len off on some of his own experiences of toadying, rackets and injustice.

He tells of an ambitious Corporal who soon became a Sergeant by waiting about for his Officer so as to offer him *The Times* which he himself never read. 'Would you care to see my paper, sir?' Of the loss of an Anson aircraft, of which Len was a crew member, off the coast of Scotland, by means of which the Warrant Officer (Stores) was able to adjust his unsteady account books from replacement of the gear supposed to have gone with her to the bottom of the sea: navigation watches, computers (both patterns), bomb sights, Very pistols, Aldis lamps and other navigational equipment; she could never have got off the deck, Len said, with the load of stuff supposed to have been on board. Of the re-mustering camp at Whitelake full of dead-legs, misfits, unfortunates and cowards, where a veteran airman ran a fiddle by hiring out his colleagues as cleaners to commercial enterprises in the town, giving them a meal and a shilling a day and pocketing the substantial balance himself. Of the meek little airman who, maddened by the size and uncertainty of his allowance on Pay Parade, threw his packet in the Officer's face, was locked up, kicked out the door of his cell, assaulted two S.P.s and received a longish glass-house sentence.

'But what brought you to 'appy Over'ill, Len?'

'Well, soon after the racket of Whitelake camp, a Flight Sergeant interviewed us for re-mustering: quite a sympathetic bloke. I tried to get "Compass Adjuster" – that's what young Bertie here ought to try for – but not having a powerful enough personality, Flight wouldn't wear it. Across my papers in large bold writing is "Permanently unfit to fly". Couldn't blame him really. He suggested Clerk S.D. "Very hush-hush; highly secret; something special. Take a chance, eh? No; I don't know anything about the trade; just know they want blokes with flying experience, blokes like you."

'Thus, to Stenge and Grey Cottage attic.

'So now I know what a let down the whole thing is: the disloyalties to gain a doubtful advantage over comrades, and above all the servile rectum exploring to obtain advancement. That's what really sickens me.'

'Well,' says Bertie fiercely, his pale blue eyes glaring, 'so long as we all three stick together we'll beat 'em in the end, won't we, Webby?'

Len lies back on his bunk, his hands clasped behind his head, and resumes his meditative silence. Then he starts to hum an ancient melody of mysterious sweetness, and three hard moods are softened for the night's sleep. Bertie moans a few sentimental words about Polly, the Waaf that he loves best. Sensing Webland's lack of enthusiasm, he adds:

'You do think she's smashing, now don't you, Webby?'

'I read the other day that a male moth can smell a female moth from a distance of seven and a half miles. Good night, you poor moth.'

'Oh, shut up, Webby.'

'Good night.'

The next morning Webland sets off for home on his ten days' leave.

It is mid-October when he reports back at Thorn Grove and most of the heat has gone out of the sunshine. Vera and he get a chance of a long talk outside the Ops Room, when he tells her news of his home and of hers near by, and she tells him that she has heard again from two Squadron Leaders at Group Headquarters that there is positively no question of a commission for Webland in Operations. If she knows why, she doesn't say.

On watch that night he is once more back as door sentry. It looks like no more learning now. A decision seems to have been taken about him. At least there is a chair and a stove and he can read and write, except that with airmen and Waafs and Officers coming and going, he is not unoccupied for more than three minutes at a time. Sergeant Jimmy invites him and one of the lads to take twenty minutes off before closing time to skip to the Three Horseshoes for a pint, and Jimmy is most agreeable, whatever secrets he may be harbouring. Sergeant Hayward, too, contrives a satirical smile and sends him off to bed soon after eleven thirty, perhaps by way of softening a blow about to fall.

Next night he is allowed to do some plotting in the Ops Room. He stands for two hours, at the other side of the map from Vera, who is having droll conversations by headphone with Officers at other sectors, his magnetic plotting rod held butt to the floor by his extended arm, ready for immediate action. Sergeant Hayward comes smiling up, pleased perhaps with prospering schemes, and says: 'Corporal Isaac says you look either like Britannia or Neptune.' Webland can think of no smart reply, but bows gravely in acknowledgement. It doesn't matter what answer Sergeant Hayward gets, since his looks always signal that he doesn't think Webland is quite all there. His reasoning may be that, when fatigues are in the offing, any airman with his wits about him is nowhere to be found, whereas Webland is always available.

At ten-thirty next morning he is told by Sergeant Hayward to report immediately to the C.O. 'Ah,' he thinks, 'at last he's going to introduce himself and help me, as Frank asked him to. Perhaps Vera has had something to do with this, too. She's always urging me to go and explain things to Sprucey.'

After ten minutes outside the door he is admitted. The C.O. is alone.

'You want to see me, sir.'

Spruce-Jones sits at his desk, pale and unsmiling, and says:

'Yes, Webland. How are you getting on?'

'Not very well yet, sir.'

'Yes: I've had a word with your Controller and others

about you, and they tell me you're not suited for the job of Deputy Controller. Have you got anything to say about that?'

This is odd, because in the four months he has been at Thorn Grove he has not often been inside the Ops Room and the Controller has never spoken to, or, so far as he knows, observed him. However, better let that pass. He answers:

'No, sir; I don't think I want to say anything about it, though I'm naturally interested to learn the opinion of those in charge of me. I suppose a Deputy Controller needs to be air-minded, to have some knowledge of aircraft, and perhaps flying experience.'

He thinks of adding: 'By the way, I've never even started doing anything of the Deputy Controllers' course', but judges it useless in the light of the way the scene is developing.

'No,' says the C.O., 'no; not that necessarily. But you want to be quick thinking, have quick reactions.'

'I see,' says Webland; 'but what's been bothering me is why I'm here at all. Here are these sparks on my arm to show I've been trained as a Radio Operator and I get posted where I've never seen a goniometer since.'

'Well, I suppose you weren't much good at that either; your work must have been unsatisfactory.'

His mind radios back to his comrades and N.C.O.s at Cadstone and Bindover and he wonders what would be their comment. 'It's the System, chum'; or perhaps something more caustic. He hazards a mild riposte to this uncomfortable young man who has been prompted to tell him such preposterous things:

'So satisfactory was my work, sir, that I was asked to stay on as a Corporal Instructor.'

'Well, that's as may be. But I definitely cannot recommend you for a commission in Operations. I am willing, however,' he adds, almost as though a physical strain had suddenly ceased, 'to recommend you for one in some other branch.'

Webland thinks: 'Well, I've been through all that over a year ago, with a better Squadron Leader, too. This is the moment of untruth. I'm obviously back at the point of no departure, or at least of inevitable return; and this isn't the way out of the maze.'

He says: 'Thank you, sir'; and is dismissed with a surprisingly light heart, as is sometimes the case when a long uncertainty ends, one way or the other.

Well, what are they going to do with him now? If he is sent overseas what is his trade when he gets there? An outdated Radio Operator, an untrained Ops erk, or a general cleaner? Or will he stay at Overhill as door-keeper for the duration?

Some sort of answer emerges three days later when one of the Flight Sergeants tells him he is to report the next day at an address in Whitehall for an interview with a Major Hill-Hampton. Why a Major? This can't be connected with the disrecommended commission. It must be something to do with Claud Marchley and his D.M.I., which he has since learnt stands for Director of Military Intelligence. Special duties, most secret, hush-hush again like that job of Len's.

Punctually at ten-thirty Webland reports at Whitehall, to be put in a waiting-room for half an hour and then told to come back at two. So far, so familiar; except that he has had a chair to sit on. In the passage outside he meets his brother-in-law, once a Member of Parliament, now dressed as a Lieutenant-Colonel, who takes him into his office and tells him that he is supposed to be enter-taining American troops but that they don't want to be entertained really, so he doesn't do any work at all. Is this true, or is it cover talk for something appallingly secret? You mustn't speak the truth too much in the Secret Service; yet Webland doesn't think David capable of sustained deception. Perhaps he is speaking the truth after all. As it is in Ops, so it may be in this building: plenty of personnel for plenty of doing nothing.

Webland reports back at two. Major Hill-Hampton

asks him whether he is prepared to do what in effect he isn't himself quite prepared to explain. Webland in his prudence tries to give an impression of being very willing to do it if he gets a more precise idea of what he cannot understand. After one or two short circular essays in conversation the interview is over. The Major might or might not let him know. Webland departs vaguely, hoping he has not let Claud down – if it was indeed Claud who had put this invisible wheel in motion. It might possibly have been Cuthbert Latimer, though.

Having five or six hours to spare before his return to camp, he thinks it would be a good idea to call on Latimer, at his office, than which there are very few more august spots in London. Suddenly confronted by Webland, Latimer, who looks as though he has had a tiresome enough day already, exclaims:

'Good God, Theodore, what on earth are you still dressed like that for? I thought you were an Officer by this time.'

'Well, I don't know if it's anything to do with your efforts to help me, but I was told a day or two ago by my Commanding Officer that I wasn't bright enough to be one.'

Almost before Webland has finished his sentence Latimer has picked up the telephone.

'Put me through to Sir Walter Puckrup at the Air Ministry.'

'Hi, Cuthbert, steady on. Let's talk about this . . .'

But there's no stopping him now. Some telephone talk ensues; and then:

'Walter wants you to go round and see him straight away. He'll expect you within half an hour. Do you know him, by the way?'

'Met him once, I think, long ago. But honestly, Cuthbert . . .'

'You'd better start off now. Let me know what happens.'

At the Ministry no one leaves him to stand in a passage

for an hour and then tells him to come back next day. He is taken straight to Puckrup's room.

After Webland has briefly told the tale of his career, Puckrup says:

'I can't tell you how sorry I am, my dear feller, for the way you've been treated. . . . Now, what do you want? Do you want to stay in the Air Force?'

'Oh, yes.' Perhaps he should have added: 'Definitely.'

'All right. You leave it to me. You'll be on your Officers' course in a matter of a week or two.'

Can there really be no mistake this time? As he sits in the train back to Stenge he still feels he can't be certain of anything any more. Yet Puckrup is closest to the Minister, and Cuthbert closest to one far above the Ministry; and Cuthbert isn't going to be made a monkey of now. It ought to be all right. But what a pity it had to be done like this.

He tells no one at Overhill of what has happened to him. Ten days pass. Len and Bertie go on seven days' leave. What about Puckrup's 'matter of a week or two' now? It was on the 10th that he had said it. Now it's the 24th and time's up.

Next afternoon, as he is standing with a knot of airmen outside Ops, one of the Sergeants comes up and says: 'Webland, you are to report to the Orderly Room at the aerodrome on the 2nd and proceed on an Officers' course on the 4th.'

Everyone seems pleased. As he walks back alone to Grey Cottage his thoughts whirl about in confusion. How will this affect the result of his interview with the double-hush Major? What will Spruce-Jones think? What does he think himself?

This is indeed a pitiable performance. So that's how to become an Officer; not by acting for fourteen months as though one were after the Sword of Honour at Cranwell. However, no cause for regret there. It has all been well worth it.

Will Len and Bertie be back from leave in time to say

good-bye? Now that he has reached his goal he begins to feel melancholy. Good-bye once more to comrades.

One thing is certain. He has had a wonderful adventure in friendship, and there cannot be anything quite like it again. After the war, be the barriers what they may, he will seek out and hold on to such of his former mates as may be alive and can be found, and never let them become mere ghosts of a disturbing dream. Yes, that is quite certain.